ART

IN THE

UNITED
STATES
CAPITOL

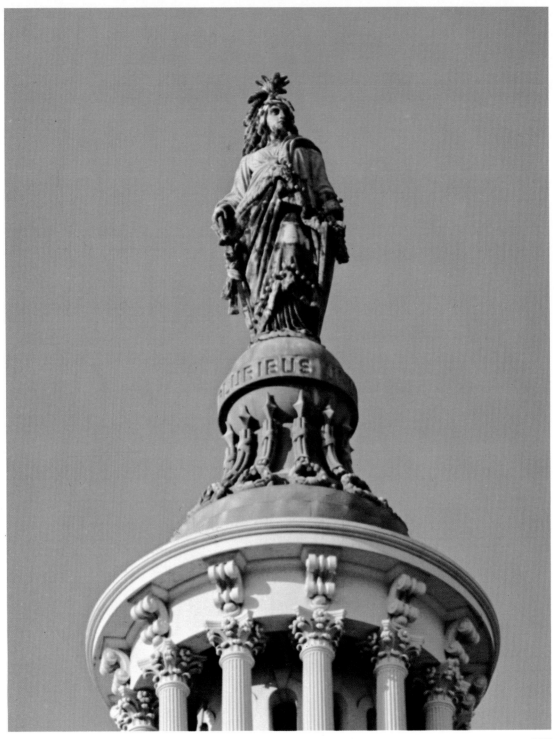

FREEDOM
Thomas Crawford
Dome of the United States Capitol

ART
IN THE
UNITED
STATES
CAPITOL

PREPARED BY
THE ARCHITECT OF THE CAPITOL
UNDER THE DIRECTION OF
THE JOINT COMMITTEE ON THE LIBRARY

UNITED STATES GOVERNMENT PRINTING OFFICE
WASHINGTON 1978

iii

Library of Congress Card Catalog Number 72–600081

For sale by the Superintendent of Documents, U.S. Government Printing Office
Washington, D.C. 20402

Stock No. 052–071–00546–3

iv

H. Con. Res. 698 Passed Oct. 1, 1976

(Submitted by Mr. Brademus)

Ninety-fourth Congress of the United States of America

CONCURRENT RESOLUTION

Resolved by the House of Representatives (the Senate concurring), That there be reprinted with black and white and color illustrations and with emendations as a House document "Art in the United States Capitol" as prepared under the direction of the Architect of the Capitol; and that there be printed thirty-six thousand four hundred additional copies of such document, of which ten thousand three hundred copies shall be for the use of the Senate, twenty-two thousand one hundred copies shall be for the use of the House of Representatives, and four thousand copies for the use of the Architect of the Capitol.

Attest:

EDMUND L. HENSHAW, JR.
Clerk of the House.

Attest:

FRANCIS R. VALEO
Secretary of the Senate.

COMMITTEE ON HOUSE ADMINISTRATION

Ninety-fourth Congress—Second Session

FRANK THOMPSON, JR., New Jersey, *Chairman*

JOHN H. DENT, Pennsylvania

WILLIAM L. DICKINSON, Alabama

LUCIEN N. NEDZI, Michigan

SAMUEL L. DEVINE, Ohio

JOHN BRADEMAS, Indiana

JAMES C. CLEVELAND, New Hampshire

AUGUSTUS F. HAWKINS, California

CHARLES E. WIGGINS, California

FRANK ANNUNZIO, Illinois

J. HERBERT BURKE, Florida

JOSEPH M. GAYDOS, Pennsylvania

W. HENSON MOORE, Louisiana

ED JONES, Tennessee

BILL FRENZELL, Minnesota

ROBERT H. MOLLOHAN, West Virginia

RON PAUL, Texas

DAWSON MATHIS, Georgia

LIONEL VAN DEERLIN, California

JOSEPH G. MINISH, New Jersey

MENDEL J. DAVIS, South Carolina

CHARLES ROSE, North Carolina

LINDY (MRS. HALE) BOGGS, Louisiana

JOHN L. BURTON, California

EDWARD W. PATTISON, New York

WILLIAM H. CABLE, *Staff Director and Associate Counsel*

ROBERT E. MOSS, *General Counsel*

JOINT COMMITTEE ON THE LIBRARY

Ninety-fourth Congress—Second Session

HOWARD W. CANNON, Senator from Nevada, *Chairman*

LUCIEN N. NEDZI, Representative from Michigan, *Vice Chairman*

FRANK THOMPSON, JR.
Representative from New Jersey

SAMUEL L. DEVINE
Representative from Ohio

JOHN BRADEMAS
Representative from Indiana

W. HENSON MOORE
Representative from Louisiana

CLAIBORNE PELL
Senator from Rhode Island

ROBERT P. GRIFFIN
Senator from Michigan

HARRISON A. WILLIAMS, JR.
Senator from New Jersey

HUGH SCOTT
Senator from Pennsylvania

WILLIAM McWHORTER COCHRANE, *Chief Clerk*

ROBERT STEWART ROYER, *Assistant Chief Clerk*

JURISDICTION OVER WORKS OF ART

Since 1872 the Joint Committee on the Library has had supervision of all works of art in the United States Capitol under the provisions of section 1831 of the Revised Statutes of the United States as follows:

The Joint Committee on the Library, whenever, in their judgment, it is expedient, are authorized to accept any work of the fine arts, on behalf of Congress, which may be offered, and to assign the same such place in the Capitol as they may deem suitable, and shall have the supervision of all works of art that may be placed in the Capitol.

REPRODUCTIONS

Negative numbers in this book are for 8″ x 10″ black and white prints only. They may be purchased by title and negative number from the Photoduplication Service, Library of Congress, Washington, D.C. 20540. Color slides, color prints and color transparencies are not available.

All photographs, with exceptions as noted, are property of the U.S. Government, Office of the Architect of the Capitol, United States Capitol, Washington, D.C. 20515.

MEASUREMENTS AND SIGNATURE LOCATIONS

Sight measurements of portraits and paintings are given with height first and width second. Measurements of busts and statues are approximate and do not include the pedestals.

The location of the artist's signature is designated by the letters u.l., u.r., l.l., and l.r., indicating upper left, upper right, lower left and lower right.

THE CAPITOL ART COLLECTION

COMPRISES A TOTAL OF 682 WORKS OF ART AS OF DECEMBER 1976

136 PORTRAITS

14 Presidents of the United States
2 Vice Presidents of the United States
22 United States Senators
46 Speakers of the House of Representatives
7 Small portraits of Speakers of the House of Representatives
24 Chairmen of the House Committee on Appropriations
8 Architects of the Capitol
13 Prominent Individuals

54 PAINTINGS:

8 in the Rotunda
12 in the Senate wing
5 in the House wing
18 in the Central section
1 in the Russell Senate Office Building
10 in the House Office Buildings

77 BUSTS:

10 Presidents of the United States
37 Vice Presidents of the United States
5 Chief Justices of the United States
4 United States Senators
10 Speakers and Members of the House of Representatives
11 Prominent Individuals

102 STATUES:

92 contributed by States to the National Statuary Hall collection
9 not contributed by States
1 Liberty and the Eagle
1 Women's Suffrage Monument

90 RELIEFS:

75 in the House Chamber:
    23 portraits of Lawgivers, 52 Seals of States and Territories
1 in the Old Supreme Court Chamber
8 in the Rotunda
3 in the Senate Chamber
3 on the East Front portico

137 FRESCOES, MURALS AND LUNETTES:

2 in the Rotunda
15 in the House wing
120 in the Senate wing

29 EXTERIOR WORKS OF ART:

4 bronze doors
1 fountain
19 statues
1 memorial
4 tympanums

57 MISCELLANEOUS WORKS OF ART:

37 sculptures:
    23 capitals, 2 clocks, 2 eagles,
    1 fountain, 1 mask, 2 statuettes,
    2 sculptural groups, 4 stairways.
4 vases
16 windows and laylights:
    7 circular, 7 rectangular,
    1 Prayer Room, 1 Washington memorial.

The objects in Appendix I and Appendix II are not included in this tabulation.

Foreword

The collection of art in the United States Capitol represents an integral part of the history of this renowned building. This edition of *Art in the United States Capitol* is the culmination of various publications issued over the past seventy years. In 1927, the first comprehensive history of the accumulation and development of art in the Capitol was compiled by art curator Charles E. Fairman. Fairman's chronological narrative, *Art and Artists of the Capitol of the United States of America*, was the forerunner of a twenty-four page catalog issued by the Architect of the Capitol in 1952. The catalog was not illustrated, but because of its thorough and concise listing, the Joint Committee on the Library published it as a joint committee print.

The Capitol art collection continued to grow and public demand for information on the subject increased. As a result, the first hardbound edition on Capitol art was released in 1965, entitled *Compilation of Works of Art and Other Objects in the United States Capitol*. That volume contained over four hundred black and white illustrations of paintings and sculptures, including reliefs, frescoes, plaques and miscellaneous objects of interest and served as a valuable reference tool.

The 1976 Bicentennial edition featured several changes, including the present title. Color photographs of the paintings replaced black and white pictures, enhancing the total beauty and value of the book. The succinct new format provides additional information not previously available in a single volume. Included in the appendix are diagrams that enable students and visitors to locate works of art in which they are interested.

I wish to recognize the particular contributions and interest of the Honorable William L. Dickinson of Alabama for his foresight in introducing the first concurrent resolution for the printing of the 1976 edition and also the Honorable John Brademas of Indiana for his leadership in seeing that the second printing of *Art in the United States Capitol* became a fact.

George M. White, Architect of the Capitol, and members of his staff headed by Florian H. Thayn and her assistant Karen L. Miles of the Art and Reference Division, are responsible for the research, text and general organization of the book. The excellent photographs, both color and black and white, are the work of Harry L. Burnett, Jr. and Mark M. Blair.

FRANK THOMPSON, JR., *Chairman*
Committee on House Administration

United States Senate

COMMITTEE ON
RULES AND ADMINISTRATION
WASHINGTON, D.C. 20510

On behalf of the Senate Committee on Rules and Administration, I am happy to join in sponsoring this new edition of *Art in the United States Capitol*, the first to illustrate most of this notable and historic collection in color. This second printing, the need for which was occasioned by the very gratifying public response to the new edition, incorporates the changes in location or accessions which have occurred during the second session of the Ninety-fourth Congress.

HOWARD W. CANNON
Chairman
Senate Committee on Rules
and Administration

Contents

Portraits

Presidents of the United States
Vice Presidents of the United States
United States Senators
Speakers of the House of Representatives
Chairmen of the House Committee on Appropriations
Architects of the Capitol
Prominent Individuals

NEG. NO. 23105

GEORGE WASHINGTON
William Dunlap, 1783, from life, pastel, 25½″ x 19½″
Gift of Mrs. A. V. H. Ellis, 1940
Accepted by the Joint Committee on the Library
SB–16

GEORGE WASHINGTON AT PRINCETON
Charles Willson Peale, 91⅝″ x 58⅜″
Signed l.l. C. W. Peale pinx, Philadelphia 1779
Purchased 1882
Senate wing, third floor, west corridor

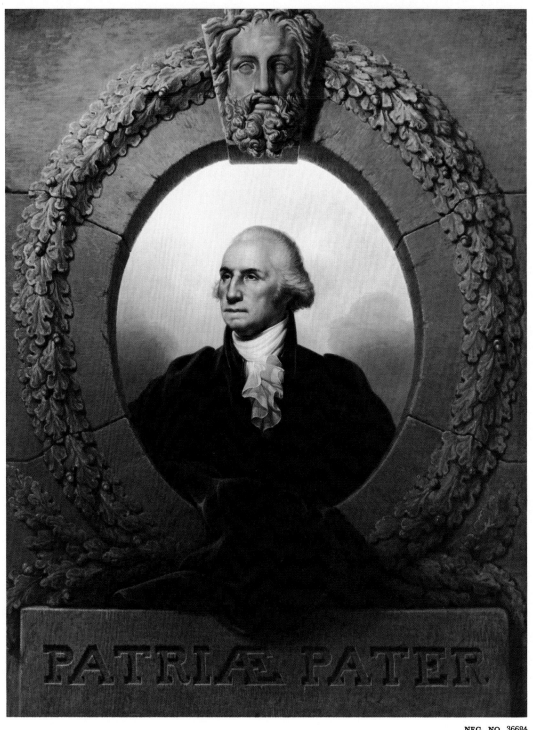

GEORGE WASHINGTON
Rembrandt Peale, 1828, from life, 69½″ x 52½″
Purchased 1832
S–228, Old Senate Chamber

GEORGE WASHINGTON
Gilbert Stuart, from life, Thomas Chestnut portrait, 28½″ x 23½″
Purchased 1876
S–207, Senators' Conference Room

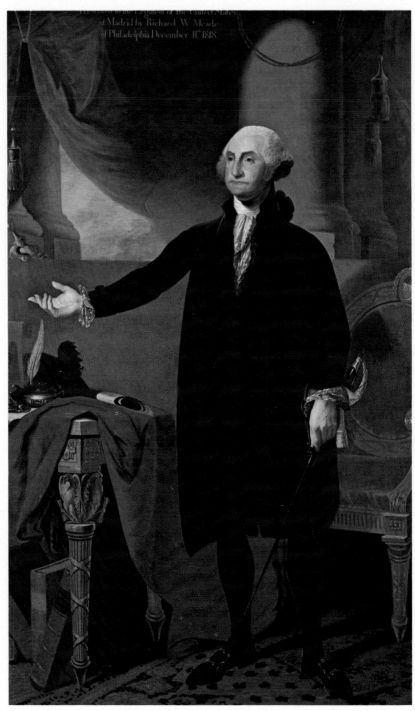

NEG. NO. 719

GEORGE WASHINGTON
Gilbert Stuart, from life, Lansdowne or "teapot" type, 93″ x 59″
Transferred from U.S. Embassy in Spain to the Capitol, 1951
Placed by authority of the Speaker
H–207, House Reception Room

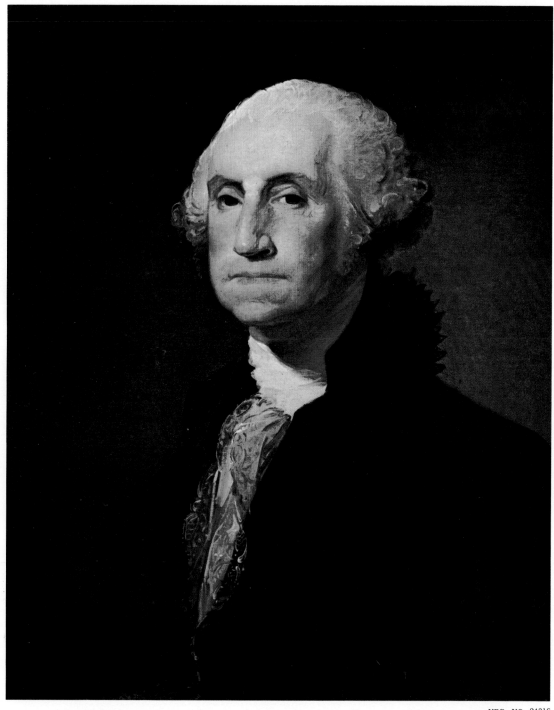

GEORGE WASHINGTON
Gilbert Stuart, from life, Edward Pennington portrait, 30″ x 25″
Purchased 1886
S–210

GEORGE WASHINGTON
John Vanderlyn, 1834, after Gilbert Stuart, 92″ x 62″
Commissioned by Resolution of June 28, 1832, 22nd Congress
House Chamber

8

NEG. NO. 23939

JOHN ADAMS
Eliphalet Frazer Andrews, 1881, after Gilbert Stuart, 29½″ x 24½″
Purchased 1881
Senate wing, second floor, main corridor

9

THOMAS JEFFERSON
Thomas Sully, 29½″ x 24½″
Signed on back TS 1856
Purchased 1874
S–210

ANDREW JACKSON
Attributed to Thomas Sully, 1845, 29½″ x 24½″
Purchased 1922 by S. Res. 75, 67th Congress
S–210

ABRAHAM LINCOLN
Antonio Salviati, mosaic, 22″ diameter
Gift of the artist, 1866
Accepted by Con. Res. of July 26, 1866, 39th Congress
S–109

NEG. NO. 23938

ABRAHAM LINCOLN
Freeman Thorp, about 1879, 28½″ x 23″
Signed u. r. Thorp
Purchased 1920 by S. Res. 292, 66th Congress
Senate wing, second floor, main corridor

13

ULYSSES S. GRANT
William Cogswell, oval, 29½'' x 24''
Signed l. center W. Cogswell, 1868
Purchased 1886
Accepted by the Joint Committee on the Library
S–210

14

JAMES A. GARFIELD
Antonio Salviati, mosaic, 24″ diameter
Signed r. center Dr. A. Salviati, Venezia 1882
Gift of the artist, 1884
Accepted by Con. Res. of May 19, 1884, 48th Congress
S–109

NEG. NO. 39580

JOHN C. CALHOUN
Henry F. Darby, about 1849, 46″ x 36″
Signed l.l. H. F. Darby
Purchased 1881
Senate wing, second floor, main corridor

JOHN NANCE GARNER
Signed 1.1. Howard Chandler Christy, 1937; 53½″ x 39½″
Purchased 1940 by P. L. 723, 75th Congress

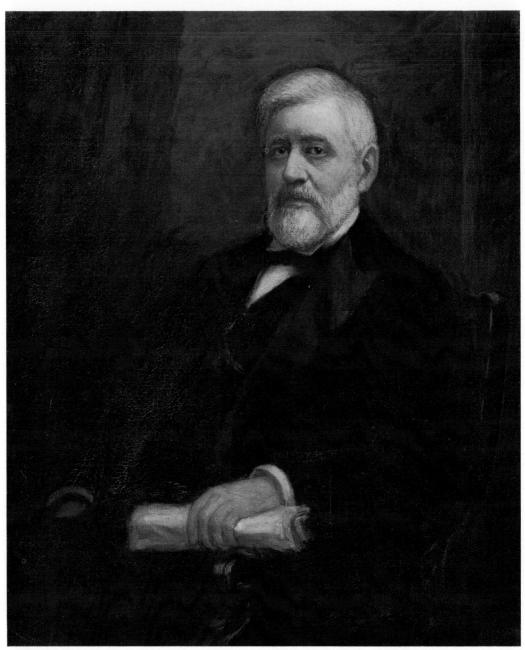

NEG. NO. 24358

WILLIAM B. ALLISON
Willbur Aaron Reaser, 41½″ x 33½″
Signed l.r. W. A. Reaser
Purchased 1909 by S. Res. 264, 60th Congress
Senate wing, second floor, main corridor

CHARLES CARROLL OF CARROLLTON
Chester Harding, 35½'' x 27½''
Purchased 1870
House wing, third floor, east corridor

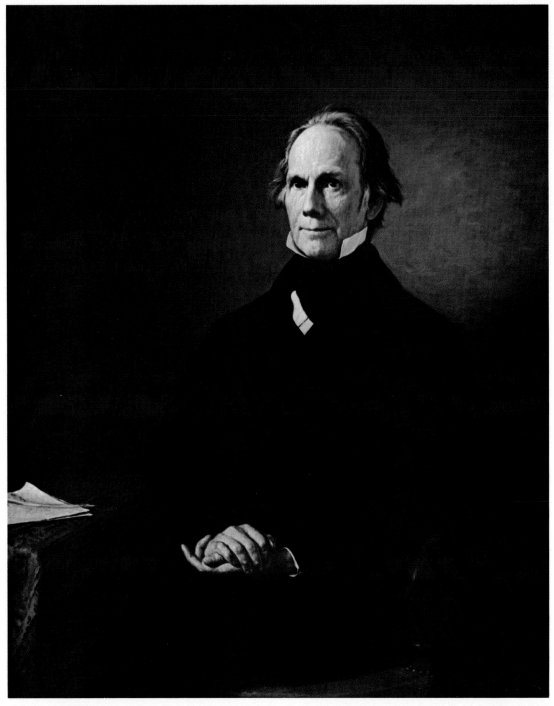

HENRY CLAY
Henry F. Darby, 50″ x 40″
Signed l.r. H. F. Darby
Purchased 1881
Senate wing, second floor, main corridor

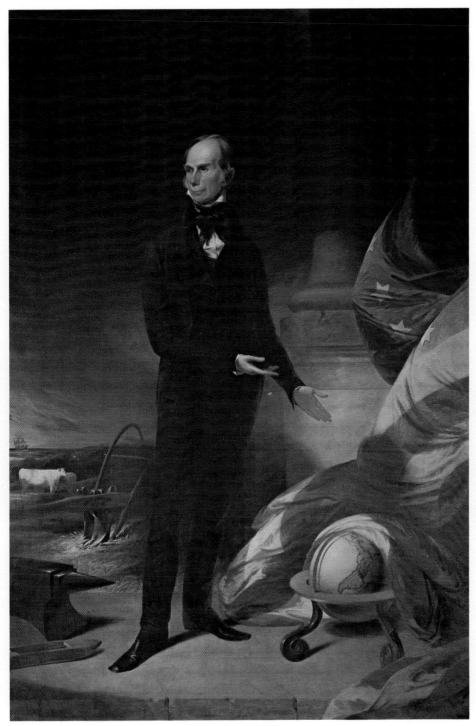

HENRY CLAY
Signed l.l. Jno. Neagle, 1843; 9′ x 5′11″
Purchased 1871
House wing, third floor, east corridor

JOHN ADAMS DIX
Signed l.l. Imogene Robinson Morrell, 1883; 50″ x 40″
Purchased 1883
In storage

ARTHUR P. GORMAN
Louis P. Dieterich, 45½" x 33"
Signed l.r. L. Dieterich, 1911
Gift of the Gorman family, 1943
Accepted by the Joint Committee on the Library
S–220

JOHN LANGDON
Hattie E. Burdette, 1916, after an engraving, 30'' x 25''
Signed l.r. H. E. Burdette
Purchased 1916 by S. Res. 118, 64th Congress
S–240

24

HENRY LATIMER
Signed l.r. Clawson S. Hammitt; 29½″ x 24½″
Gift of Mary Latimer, 1916
Accepted by the Joint Committee on the Library
Senate wing, third floor, south corridor

25

JAMES HAMILTON LEWIS
Signed u.l. Louis Betts; 39½″ x 29″
Gift of Mrs. Lewis, 1940
Accepted by the Joint Committee on the Library
Senate wing, second floor, south corridor

26

CHARLES L. MCNARY
Henrique Medina, 39½″ x 29½″
Signed u.r. H. Medina, 1946
Gift of friends, 1944
Accepted by the Joint Committee on the Library
Senate wing, second floor, main corridor

JUSTIN S. MORRILL
Eastman Johnson, 25″ x 21″
Signed l.l. E. Johnson, 1884
Gift of Louise S. Swan, 1920
Accepted by the Joint Committee on the Library
Senate wing, second floor, main corridor

28

JOSEPH T. ROBINSON
Nicholas R. Brewer, 43″ x 31½″
Signed l.l. N. R. Brewer, 1934
Gift of friends, 1937
Accepted by S. Res. 173, 75th Congress
Senate wing, second floor, main corridor

29

MORRIS SHEPPARD
Signed l.r. Boris B. Gordon—1941; 41½″ x 33½″
Gift of the Sheppard family, 1941
Accepted by S. Res. 197, 77th Congress
In storage

CHARLES SUMNER
Walter Ingalls, 43½″ x 35½″
Signed l.r. W. Ingalls, Pinxt 1876
Purchased 1886
Senate wing, second floor, main corridor

ALLEN G. THURMAN
John H. Witt
Purchased 1896 by S. Res. of January 10, 1896, 54th Congress
Location unknown. No photograph

DANIEL WEBSTER
John Neagle, 50″ x 40″
Purchased 1881
Senate wing, second floor, main corridor

DANIEL WEBSTER
James Henry Wright, 50″ x 40″
Signed l.r. J. H. Wright, N.Y.
Gift of Lester Martin, 1944
Accepted by S. Res. 330, 78th Congress
Senate wing, stairwell opposite S–216

33

When Constantino Brumidi decorated the walls of the Senate Reception Room, S–213, in the 1860's, he left unadorned areas for medallion portraits of great men yet to come. In 1956 by special legislation[1] provision was made to have the portraits of five great Senators painted in oil. Each measures 22½'' x 19½''. The unveiling was March 12, 1959.

NEG. NO. 34269

JOHN C. CALHOUN, South Carolina
Arthur Conrad

---

[1] S. Res. 297, 84th Congress (July 12, 1956) and S. Res. 174, 84th Congress (August 26, 1957).

ROBERT M. LA FOLLETTE, SR., Wisconsin
Chester LA Follette

HENRY CLAY, Kentucky
Allyn Cox

DANIEL WEBSTER, Massachusetts
Adrian Lamb

ROBERT A. TAFT, Ohio
Deane Keller

36

SPEAKERS OF THE HOUSE OF REPRESENTATIVES

FORTY-SIX PORTRAITS

This collection includes all Speakers of the House of Representatives from Speaker Muhlenberg of the First Congress through Speaker Albert of the Ninety-fourth Congress. These portraits are located in the Speaker's Lobby, House wing, second floor.

In earlier days the portraits of former Speakers were received through donations, but since 1910 provision has been made for the painting of the portrait of each Speaker during his incumbency. These portraits are hung without ceremony, usually at the close of the Speaker's term of office. The payment date is generally used as the date of purchase for this collection. According to Government procedure, the portrait would have been delivered, although it might not have been hung, by the time payment was made.

The chronological list of Speakers is followed by the portraits which are shown alphabetically.

Speaker	State	Period of service	Artist	Date of acquisition
Frederick A. C. Muhlenberg	Pennsylvania	1789–91; 1793–95	Samuel B. Waugh after Joseph Wright	1881
Jonathan Trumbull	Connecticut	1791–93	H. I. Thompson	1880
Jonathan Dayton	New Jersey	1795–99	Henry Harrison	1911
Theodore Sedgwick	Massachusetts	1799–1801	Edgar Parker	1888
Nathaniel Macon	North Carolina	1801–07	Robert D. Gauley	1911
Joseph B. Varnum	Massachusetts	1807–11	Charles L. Elliott	1888
Henry Clay	Kentucky	1811–14; 1815–20; 1823–25	Giuseppe Fagnani	1852
Langdon Cheves	South Carolina	1814–15	Hal Morrison	1912
John W. Taylor	New York	1820–21; 1825–27	Caroline L. O. Ransom	1900
Philip P. Barbour	Virginia	1821–23	Kate F. Edwards	1911
Andrew Stevenson	Virginia	1827–34	Spencer B. Nichols	1911
John Bell	Tennessee	1834–35	Willie B. Newman	1911
James K. Polk	Tennessee	1835–39	Rebecca Polk	1911
Robert M. T. Hunter	Virginia	1839–41	Richard N. Brooke	1911
John White	Kentucky	1841–43	Gerard Barry	1911
John W. Jones	Virginia	1843–45	James B. Sword	1911
John W. Davis	Indiana	1845–47	W. D. Murphy	1911
Robert C. Winthrop	Massachusetts	1847–49	Daniel Huntington	1882
Howell Cobb	Georgia	1849–51	Lucy Stanton	1912
Linn Boyd	Kentucky	1851–55	Stanley Middleton	1911
Nathaniel P. Banks	Massachusetts	1855–57	Robert Vonnoh	1888
James L. Orr	South Carolina	1857–59	Esther Edmonds	1911
William Pennington	New Jersey	1859–61	Joseph Lauber	1911
Galusha A. Grow	Pennsylvania	1861–63	William A. Greaves	1892
Schuyler Colfax	Indiana	1863–68	Freeman Thorp	1911
Theodore M. Pomeroy	New York	1868–69	George L. Clough	1921
James G. Blaine	Maine	1869–75	Freeman Thorp	1905
Michael C. Kerr	Indiana	1875–76	Charles A. Gray	1911
Samuel J. Randall	Pennsylvania	1876–81	William A. Greaves	1892
J. Warren Keifer	Ohio	1881–83	Charles A. Gray	1911
John G. Carlisle	Kentucky	1883–89	Ellen D. Hale	1911
Thomas B. Reed	Maine	1889–91; 1895–99	John S. Sargent	1891
Charles F. Crisp	Georgia	1891–95	Robert Hinckley	1894
David B. Henderson	Iowa	1899–1903	Freeman Thorp	1913
Joseph G. Cannon	Illinois	1903–11	William T. Smedley	1917
Champ Clark	Missouri	1911–19	Boris B. Gordon	1919
Frederick H. Gillett	Massachusetts	1919–25	Edmund C. Tarbell	1925
Nicholas Longworth	Ohio	1925–31	Robert Doblhoff	1930
John N. Garner	Texas	1931–33	Seymour M. Stone	1940
Henry T. Rainey	Illinois	1933–34	Howard C. Christy	1936
Joseph W. Byrns	Tennessee	1935	Ella S. Hergesheimer	1937
William B. Bankhead	Alabama	1936–39	Howard C. Christy	1938
Sam Rayburn	Texas	1940–46; 1949–52; 1955–61	Douglas Chandor	1942
Joseph W. Martin, Jr.	Massachusetts	1947–48; 1953–54	Boris B. Gordon	1959
John W. McCormack	Massachusetts	1962–71	Victor Lallier	1962
Carl B. Albert	Oklahoma	1971–77	Charles B. Wilson	1973

CARL ALBERT, Speaker
Charles Banks Wilson
Purchased 1973 by Public Law 92–342

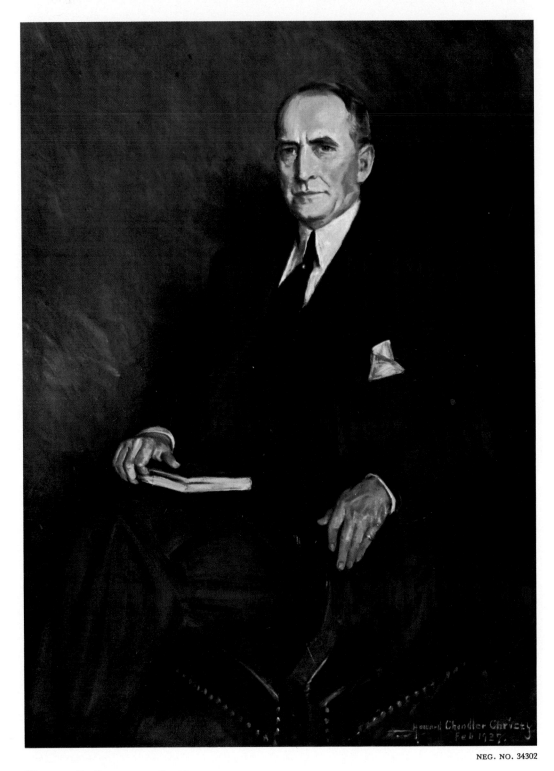

WILLIAM B. BANKHEAD, Speaker
Signed l.r. Howard Chandler Christy, Feb. 1937; 53″ x 39″
Purchased 1937 by Public No. 4, 75th Congress

NATHANIEL P. BANKS, Speaker
Signed l.l. Robt. W. Vonnoh, Boston, 1887; 49″ x 31½″
Gift of State of Massachusetts, 1888
Accepted by H. Res. of January 19, 1888, 50th Congress

PHILIP P. BARBOUR, Speaker
Kate Flournoy Edwards, 1911, 29½″ x 24½″
Purchased 1911 by H. Res. 163, 61st Congress

NEG. NO. 34305

JOHN BELL, Speaker
Willie Betty Newman, 30″ x 24½″
Signed l.r. W. B. Newman, 1911
Purchased 1911 by H. Res. 163, 61st Congress

JAMES G. BLAINE, Speaker
Freeman Thorp, 29½'' x 24''
Signed l.l. Thorp, 1905
Purchased through private contributions

NEG. NO. 34307

LINN BOYD, Speaker
Signed u.r. Stanley Middleton, 1911; 29½″ x 24½″
Purchased 1911 by H. Res. 163, 61st Congress

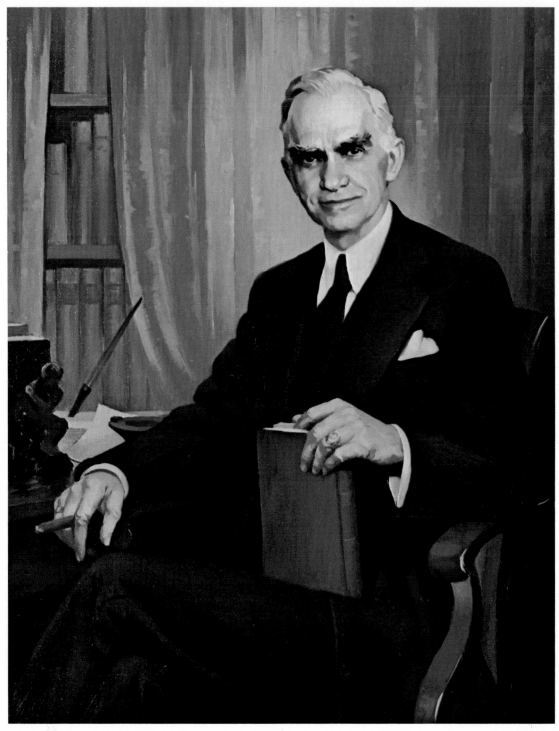

Joseph W. Byrns, Speaker
Signed l.r. E. Sophonisba Hergesheimer, 1937 ©; 45″ x 35″
Purchased 1937 by Public No. 4, 75th Congress

46

JOSEPH G. CANNON, Speaker
William T. Smedley, 55″ x 35″
Signed u.l. W. T. Smedley 1912
Purchased 1917 by Public No. 2, 65th Congress

JOHN G. CARLISLE, Speaker
Ellen Day Hale, 1911, 41″ x 33″
Purchased 1911 by H. Res. 163, 61st Congress

LANGDON CHEVES, Speaker
Signed l.l. Hal Morrison; 1912, 29½″ x 24½″
Purchased 1911 by H. Res. 163, 61st Congress

CHAMP CLARK, Speaker
Signed l.l. Boris B. Gordon, 1919; 47½″ x 33½″
Purchased 1919 by Public No. 275, 65th Congress

HENRY CLAY, Speaker
Giuseppe Fagnani, oval, 27½″ x 21½″
Signed center r. Fagnani, 1852
Gift of the artist, 1852
Accepted by Jt. Res. No. 13, 32nd Congress

HOWELL COBB, Speaker
Signed u.r. Lucy M. Stanton; 1912, 29½″ x 24½″
Purchased 1911 by H. Res. 163, 61st Congress

SCHUYLER COLFAX, Speaker
Freeman Thorp, 1911, 29½″ x 24″
Purchased 1911 by H. Res. 163, 61st Congress

53

CHARLES F. CRISP, Speaker
Robert Hinckley, 41½″ x 31″
Purchased about 1894

54

John W. Davis, Speaker
Signed u.l. W. D. Murphy, N.Y., 1911; 29½″ x 24½″
Purchased 1911 by H. Res. 163, 61st Congress

JONATHAN DAYTON, Speaker
Signed l.r. Henry Harrison, 1911; 29½″ x 24½″
Purchased 1911 by H. Res. 163, 61st Congress

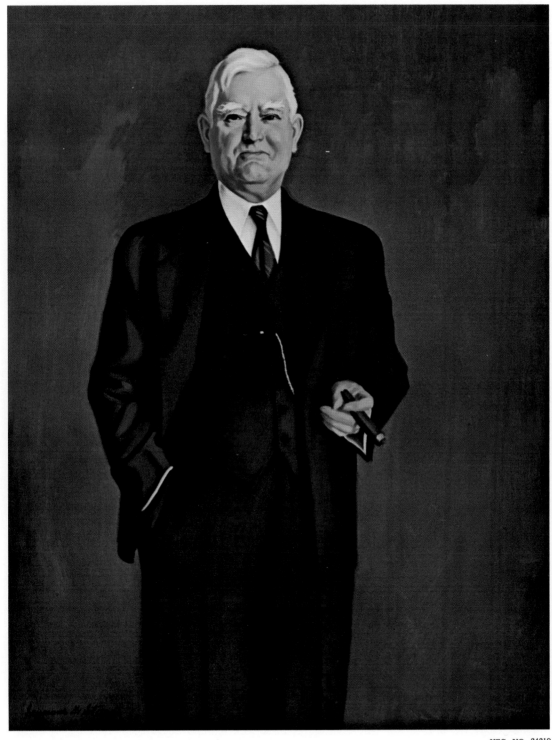

JOHN NANCE GARNER, Speaker
Signed l.l. Seymour M. Stone, 1939; 44½'' x 34½''
Acquired 1940 by H. Res. 374, 76th Congress

57

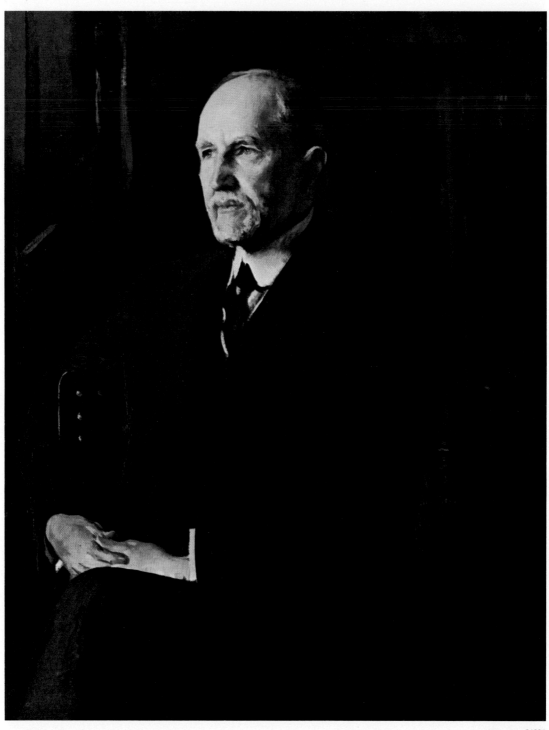

FREDERICK H. GILLETT, Speaker
Edmund C. Tarbell, 41½″ x 31½″
Signed l.r. Tarbell, 1920
Purchased 1925 by P.L. 631, 68th Congress

NEG. NO. 34321

GALUSHA A. GROW, Speaker
Signed l.r. Wm. A. Greaves, 1891; 45″ x 33″
Gift of State of Pennsylvania, 1892
Accepted by H. Res. of January 21, 1892, 52nd Congress

59

NEG. NO. 34322

DAVID B. HENDERSON, Speaker
Freeman Thorp, 29″ x 24″
Signed u.r. Thorp, 1903
Purchased 1913

60

ROBERT M. T. HUNTER, Speaker
Richard N. Brooke, 1911, 31½″ x 26½″
Signed l.r. R. N. Brooke
Purchased 1911 by H. Res. 163, 61st Congress

John W. Jones, Speaker
James B. Sword, 29½″ x 24½″
Signed l.r. J. B. Sword, 1911
Purchased 1911 by H. Res. 163, 61st Congress

J. WARREN KEIFER, Speaker
Signed l.r. Chas. A. Gray; 45½″ x 35″
Purchased 1911 by H. Res. 163, 61st Congress

63

MICHAEL KERR, Speaker
Signed l.l. Chas. A. Gray, 1911; 29½″ x 24½″
Purchased 1911 by H. Res. 163, 61st Congress

NEG. NO. 34327

Nicholas Longworth, Speaker
Robert Doblhoff, 53″ x 35½″
Signed l.l. Doblhoff, 1930
Purchased 1930 by Public No. 519, 71st Congress

NATHANIEL MACON, Speaker
Robert D. Gauley, 1911, after W. G. Randall, 29″ x 24″
Purchased 1911 by H. Res. 163, 61st Congress

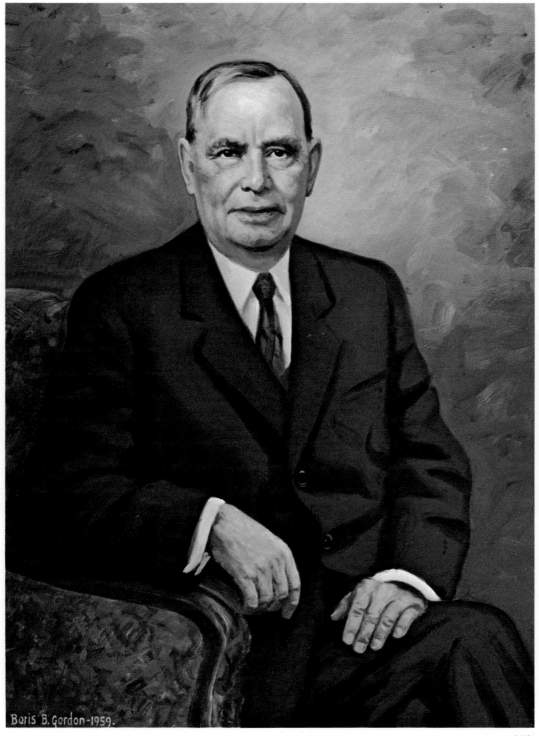

JOSEPH W. MARTIN, JR., Speaker
Signed l.l. Boris B. Gordon, 1959; 39½″ x 29½″
Purchased 1948 by P.L. 519, 80th Congress

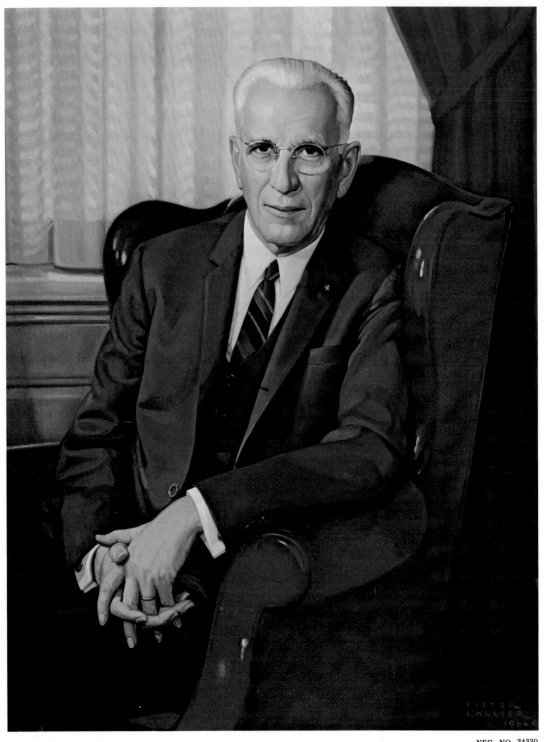

JOHN W. McCORMACK, Speaker
Signed l.r. Victor Lallier, 1966 ©; 39½″ x 29½″
Purchased 1962 by P.L. 87–730, 87th Congress

FREDERICK A. C. MUHLENBERG, Speaker
Samuel B. Waugh, after Joseph Wright, 48½″ x 36″
Signed l.r. Waugh, copy 1881
Gift of State of Pennsylvania, 1881
Accepted by H. Res. of February 26, 1881, 46th Congress

JAMES L. ORR, Speaker
Esther Edmonds, 1911, 29½″ x 24½″
Signed l.r. Edmonds
Purchased 1911 by H. Res. 163, 61st Congress

WILLIAM PENNINGTON, Speaker
Signed u.r. Jos. Lauber, 1911; 31½″ x 25″
Purchased 1911 by H. Res. 163, 61st Congress

71

JAMES K. POLK, Speaker
Rebecca Polk, 1911, after G. P. A. Healy, 30½″ x 25″
Purchased 1911 by H. Res. 163, 61st Congress

THEODORE M. POMEROY, Speaker
George L. Clough, 26½″ x 21″
Purchased 1921 by H. Res. 389, 66th Congress

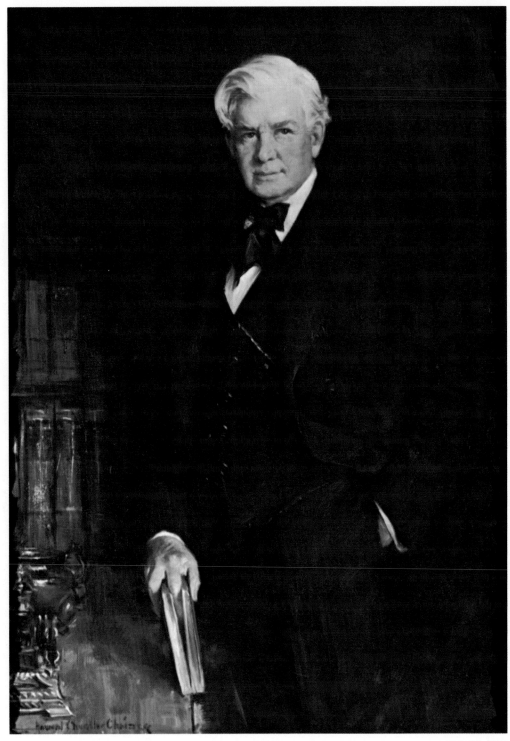

HENRY T. RAINEY, Speaker
Signed l.l. Howard Chandler Christy, 1935; 56½" x 38½"
Purchased 1935 by P.L. 200, 74th Congress

Samuel J. Randall, Speaker
Signed l.l. Wm. A. Greaves, 1891; after C. A. Fassett, 35½″ x 28½″
Gift of State of Pennsylvania, 1892
Accepted by H. Res. of January 21, 1892, 52nd Congress

SAM RAYBURN, Speaker
Douglas Chandor, 46½″ x 39″
Signed l.l. Chandor, 1941
Purchased 1941 by P.L. 145, 77th Congress

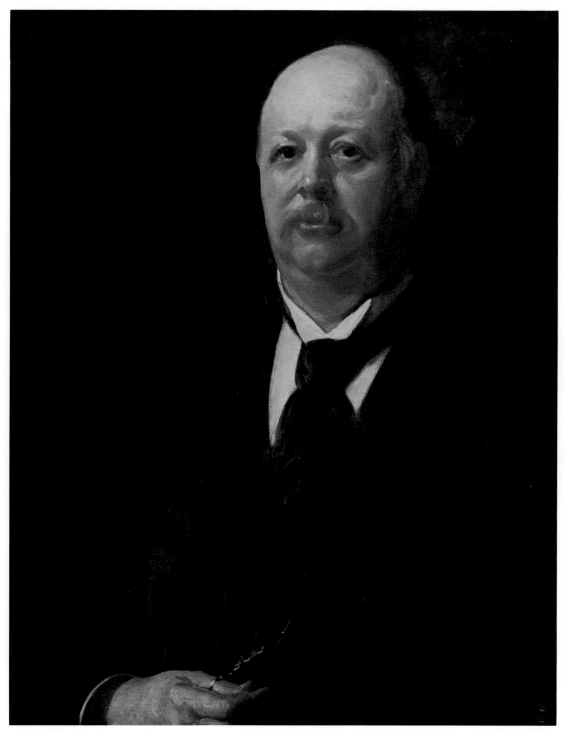

THOMAS B. REED, Speaker
Signed u.l. John S. Sargent, 1891; 31″ x 25″
Gift of Members of the 51st Congress, 1891

77

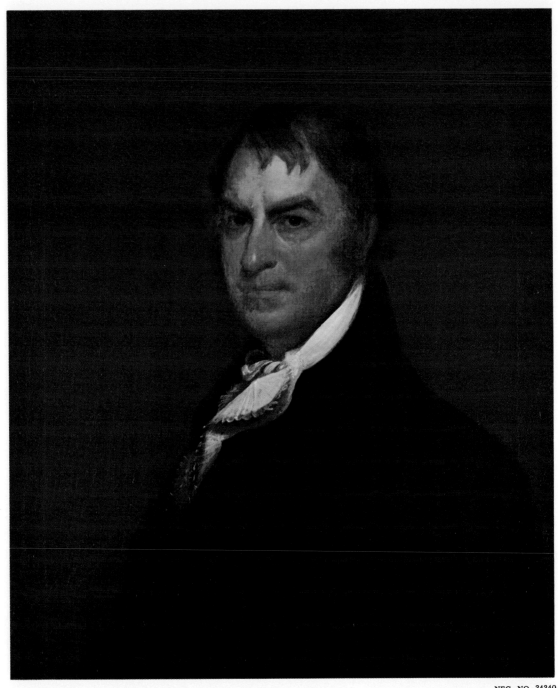

THEODORE SEDGWICK, Speaker
Edgar Parker, after Gilbert Stuart, 29½″ x 24½″
Gift of State of Massachusetts, 1888
Accepted by H. Res. of January 19, 1888, 50th Congress

ANDREW STEVENSON, Speaker
Spencer Baird Nichols, 1911, 31½″ x 26″
Signed u.r. S. B. N.
Purchased 1911 by H. Res. 163, 61st Congress

79

John W. Taylor, Speaker
Caroline L. O. Ransom, 31½″ x 25″
Purchased 1900

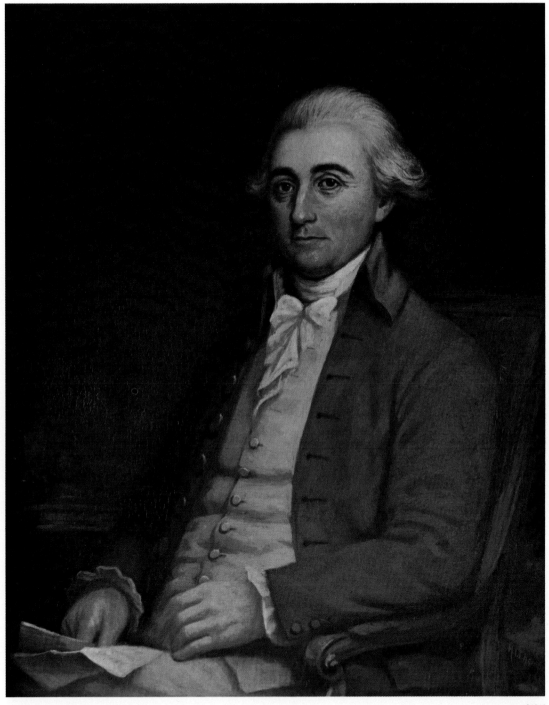

JONATHAN TRUMBULL, Speaker
Harry Ives Thompson, 35½″ x 28″
Signed l.r. H. I. Thompson, 1880
Gift of State of Connecticut, 1880
Accepted by H. Res. of December 21, 1880, 46th Congress

JOSEPH B. VARNUM, Speaker
Charles L. Elliott, 39½″ x 33½″
Gift of State of Massachusetts, 1888
Accepted by H. Res. of January 19, 1888, 50th Congress

JOHN WHITE, Speaker
Signed l.l. Gerard Barry, copy, 1911; 29½″ x 24½″
Purchased 1911 by H. Res. 163, 61st Congress

ROBERT C. WINTHROP, Speaker
Daniel Huntington, 57½″ x 37½″
Gift of Citizens of Massachusetts, 1882
Accepted by H. Res. of June 27, 1882, 47th Congress

SPEAKERS OF THE HOUSE OF REPRESENTATIVES

SEVEN SMALL PORTRAITS

A collection of seven small portraits hangs in the office of the Speaker of the House, room H–210. There are no records of their acquisition, but it is known that they were hanging in the private office of the Speaker prior to 1900. It is a tradition that these seven portraits were the incentive for the present collection in the Speaker's Lobby. With two exceptions, these small portraits are lithographs.

NEG. NO. 32240

JOHN BELL
Charles Fenderich, 1841 13″ x 9″

NEG. NO. 32241

LINN BOYD
Unknown lithographer, 13″ x 9″

NEG. NO. 32242

JONATHAN DAYTON
Pencil or watered ink, 15½″ x 13″

85

JAMES K. POLK
Charles Fenderich, 1838 13″ x 9″

ANDREW STEVENSON
Unknown lithographer, 13″ x 9″

JOHN W. TAYLOR
Unknown artist, after Gibson, oil, 10½″ x 8½″
Acquired 1855–1857

ROBERT C. WINTHROP
Unknown lithographer, 13″ x 9″

86

CHAIRMEN OF THE HOUSE COMMITTEE ON APPROPRIATIONS

TWENTY-FOUR PORTRAITS

Portraits of 24 chairmen hang in the rooms of the House Committee on Appropriations. The collection includes all chairmen from Thaddeus Stevens of the 39th Congress through George H. Mahon of the 94th Congress. The portraits were gifts to the committee from members or friends.

It was the view of members of the Appropriations Committee and the Joint Committee on the Library that these portraits, photographs and engravings belonged to the committee, as distinguished from the House, the Senate or the Congress. They were formally offered by committee resolution to the Joint Committee on the Library November 18, 1940, on behalf of Congress as an addition to the art collection of the Capitol.

In 1971 the Joint Committee on the Library accepted the photograph of Thaddeus Stevens and the portraits of Clarence Cannon and John Taber. The portrait of Chairman Mahon was accepted in 1974.

Chairman	State	Service	Artist
Thaddeus Stevens	Pennsylvania	1865–68	Mathew Brady
Elihu B. Washburne	Illinois	1868–69	Engraving
Henry L. Dawes	Massachusetts	1869–71	Photograph
James A. Garfield	Ohio	1871–75	C. Adele Fassett
Samuel J. Randall	Pennsylvania	1875–76; 1883–89	Kathryne C. Dimmitt
William S. Holman	Indiana	1876–77; 1891–93	Engraving
John D. C. Atkins	Tennessee	1877–81	Photograph
Frank Hiscock	New York	1881–83	Photograph
Joseph G. Cannon	Illinois	1889–91; 1895–1903	Freeman Thorp
Joseph D. Sayers	Texas	1893–95	Photograph
James A. Hemenway [1]	Indiana	1903–05	Photograph
James A. Tawney	Minnesota	1905–11	Freeman Thorp
John J. Fitzgerald	New York	1911–17	Kenyon Cox
J. Swagar Sherley	Kentucky	1918–19	Charles S. Williams
James W. Good	Iowa	1919–21	John C. Johansen
Martin B. Madden	Illinois	1921–28	Underwood and Underwood
Daniel R. Anthony	Kansas	1928–29	Photograph
William R. Wood	Indiana	1929–31	George B. Matthews
Joseph W. Byrns	Tennessee	1931–33	George B. Matthews
James P. Buchanan	Texas	1933–37	Seymour M. Stone
Edward T. Taylor	Colorado	1937–41; 1941–46	John C. Johansen
John Taber	New York	1947–48; 1953–54	Frank de Bruin Valerius
Clarence Cannon	Missouri	1949–52; 1955–64	Charles J. Fox
George H. Mahon	Texas	1964–	Charles J. Fox

[1] No photograph. Location unknown.

DANIEL R. ANTHONY, Chairman 1928–1929
Photograph
H–217

John D. C. Atkins, Chairman 1877–1881
Photograph
In storage

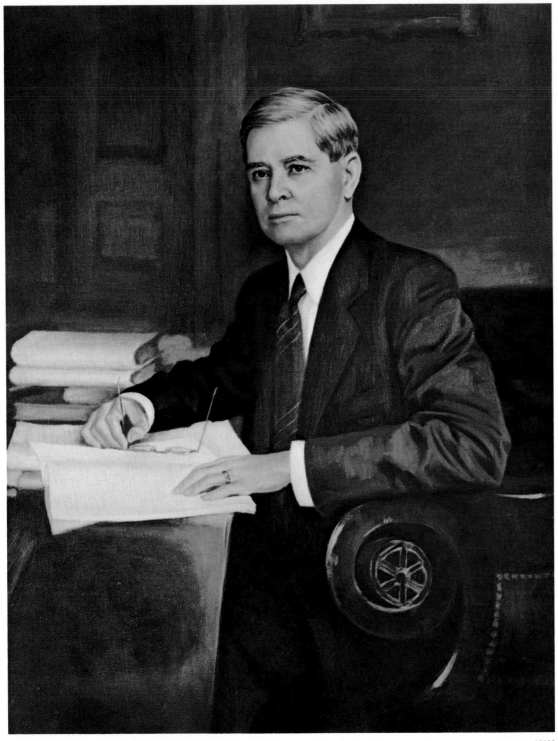

JAMES P. BUCHANAN, Chairman 1933–1937
Signed l.l. Seymour M. Stone, 1946; 39½″ x 29½″
H–218

NEG. NO. 22873

JOSEPH W. BYRNS, Chairman 1931–1933
George B. Matthews, 39½″ x 29½″
Signed l.r. G. B. Matthews 1933
H–217

CLARENCE CANNON, Chairman 1941–46, 1949–52, 1955–64
Charles J. Fox, 29½″ x 24½″
Signed l.r. C J Fox
H–218

JOSEPH G. CANNON, Chairman 1889–1891, 1895–1903
Freeman Thorp, 40″ x 31″
Signed l.l. Thorp, 1914
H–216

HENRY L. DAWES, Chairman 1869–1871
Photograph
In storage

JOHN J. FITZGERALD, Chairman 1911–1917
Signed u.r. Kenyon Cox, 1917; 25½″ x 20½″
H–217

JAMES A. GARFIELD, Chairman 1871–1875
Signed l.r. C Adèle Fassett, 1891; 53½″ x 33½″
H–216

NEG. NO. 24034

JAMES W. GOOD, Chairman 1919–1921
Signed u.l. John C. Johansen, 1921; 39½″ x 35″
H–217

FRANK HISCOCK, Chairman 1881–1883
Photograph
In storage

WILLIAM S. HOLMAN, Chairman 1876–1877, 1891–1893
Engraving
In storage

MARTIN B. MADDEN, Chairman, 1921–1928
Signed l.r. Underwood & Underwood, 1926; 39½″ x 29″
H–217

100

NEG. NO. 38587

George H. Mahon, Chairman 1964–
Charles J. Fox, 1974, 39½″ x 29½″
Signed l.r. C J Fox
H–216

Joseph D. Sayers, Chairman 1893–1895
Photograph
In storage

Samuel J. Randall, Chairman 1875–1876,
   1883–1889
Kathryne C. Dimmitt, 1962, after C. A. Fassett,
   25″ x 19″
Signed l.l. K. C. Dimmitt
H–216

102

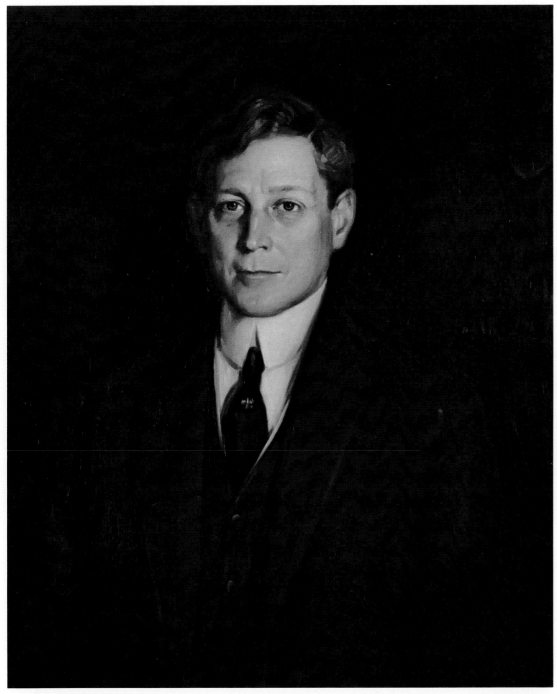

NEG. NO. 24032

J. Swagar Sherley, Chairman 1918–1919
Signed u.r. Chas. Sneed Williams; 30″ x 25″
H–217

THADDEUS STEVENS, Chairman 1865–1868
Mathew Brady, photograph oil tinted, 24½″ x 18½″
H–216

NEG. NO. 34592

JOHN TABER, Chairman 1947–48, 1953–54
Frank de Bruin Valerius, 39¼″ x 29½″
Signed u.r. Valerius—Toronto—1960
H–218

JAMES A. TAWNEY, Chairman 1905–1911
Freeman Thorp, 42¾″ x 29½″
Signed l.l. Thorp, 1911
In storage

EDWARD T. TAYLOR, Chairman 1937–1941
Signed l.r. John C. Johansen, 1939; 39½″ x 29½″
H–218

107

ELIHU B. WASHBURNE, Chairman 1868–1869
Engraving
In storage

William R. Wood, Chairman 1929–1931
George B. Matthews, 29½″ x 24½″
H–217

NEG. NO. 34282

WILLIAM THORNTON, 1793–94
George B. Matthews, after Gilbert Stuart, 29½″ x 24½″
Signed l.l. Copy by Matthews, 1930
Acquired through employment of the artist at the Capitol, 1931
SB–14

BENJAMIN H. LATROBE, 1803–11, 1815–17
George B. Matthews, after C. W. Peale, 29½″ x 24½″
Signed l.l. Matthews
Acquired through employment of the artist at the Capitol, 1931
SB–14

111

CHARLES BULFINCH, 1818–29
George B. Matthews, after 1842 drawing by Alvan Clark, 29½″ x 24½″
Signed l.r. Matthews
Acquired through employment of the artist at the Capitol, 1931
SB–14

THOMAS U. WALTER, 1851–65
Francisco Pausas, 1925, after a Brady photograph, 30″ x 23½″
Signed l.r. F. Pausas
Gift of grandson Clark Walter, 1926
SB–14

EDWARD CLARK, 1865–1902
Constantino Brumidi, 35½″ x 28½″
Gift of the Clark family, 1929
Accepted by the Joint Committee on the Library
SB–15

ELLIOTT WOODS, 1902–23
George B. Matthews, 29½″ x 24½″
Acquired through employment of the artist at the Capitol, 1931
SB–15

DAVID LYNN, 1923–54
Charles J. Fox, 1954, 29½'' x 24½''
Signed l.r. C. J. Fox
Purchased 1956 by P. L. 624, 84th Congress
SB–15

116

J. GEORGE STEWART, 1954–70
Charles J. Fox, 29½″ x 24½″
Signed l.r. C. J. Fox
Gift of the Stewart family, 1970
Accepted by the Joint Committee on the Library
SB–15

PROMINENT INDIVIDUALS
ELEVEN PORTRAITS

NEG. NO. 32187

Gunning Bedford, Jr.
Charles Willson Peale, 34″ x 26″
Bequest of Henrietta Bedford, 1872
House wing, third floor, east corridor

Delegate to the Continental Congress from Delaware 1783–85; member of the Constitutional Convention at Philadelphia in 1787 and signer of the Constitution.

118

CARLO FRANZONI
Pietro Bonanni, 19″ x 15″
Signed on reverse Bonani, pinxt 1818
Gift of Dr. Charles H. Franzoni, 1924
Accepted by the Joint Committee on the Library
HB–29

Sculptor, native of Carrara, Italy. Came to Washington, D.C. about 1816, died 1819. His chief works are the Car of History clock and the relief of Justice.

119

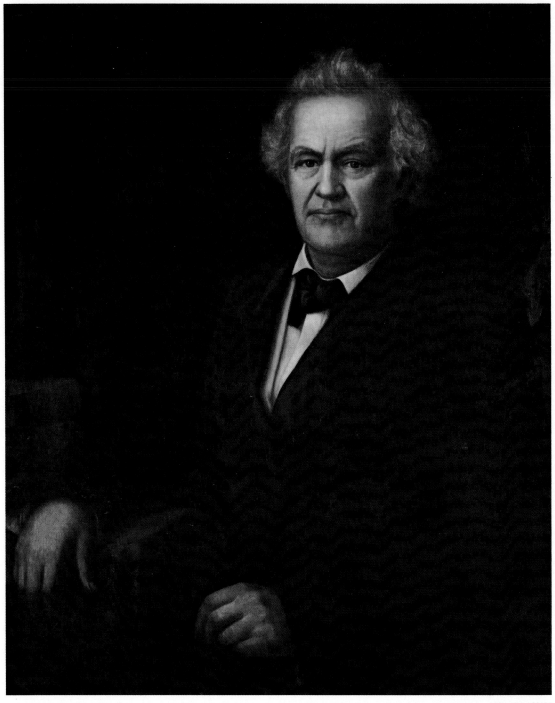

JOSHUA R. GIDDINGS
Caroline L. Ormes Ransom, 39½″ x 31½″
Purchased 1867
In storage

A Representative from Ohio; served in Congress intermittently from 1838 to 1859.

PATRICK HENRY
George B. Matthews, after Thomas Sully, 29½″ x 24½″
Signed l.l. G. Matthews
Acquired through employment of the artist at the Capitol, about 1900
Senate wing, second floor, main corridor

Delegate to the Continental Congress from Virginia 1774–76; American statesman and orator; Governor of Virginia.

JOHN PAUL JONES
George B. Matthews, after C. W. Peale, 44″ x 32″
Purchased 1891
212 Richard Brevard Russell Office Building

American Naval Officer in the Revolutionary War; founder of the American Navy; flew the first American flag ever shown on a regular man-of-war. Died in France in the diplomatic service.

GENERAL LAFAYETTE
Ary Scheffer, 92″ x 62″
Signed l.r. A. Scheffer 1823
Gift of the artist to the House of Representatives, 1824
House Chamber

French statesman and military officer; served as a volunteer under General Washington
in the American Revolution.

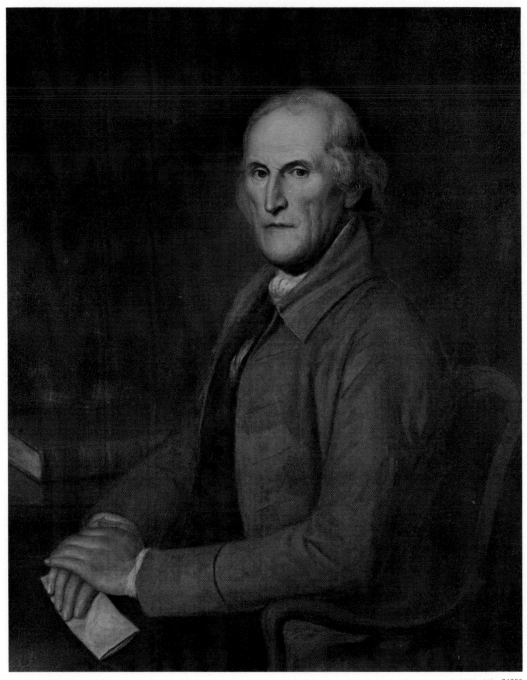

JAMES LATIMER
Clawson Shakespeare Hammitt, 35½″ x 28½″
Gift of Mary Latimer, 1916
Accepted by the Joint Committee on the Library
Senate wing, third floor, south corridor

Lieutenant Colonel in the Continental Army; presided over the Delaware Convention, the first State to ratify the Constitution; lawyer.

124

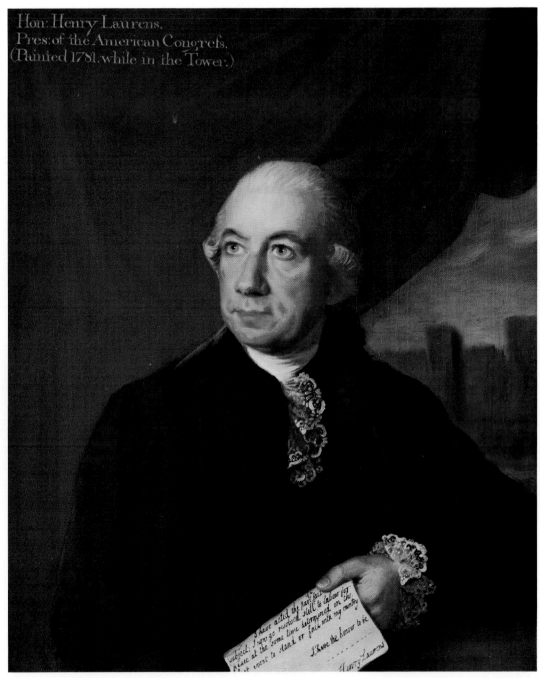

Hon: Henry Laurens.
Pres: of the American Congres.
(Painted 1781. while in the Tower.)

NEG. NO. 34000

HENRY LAURENS
Attributed to John Singleton Copley, 1781, 30″ x 25″
Purchased 1886
S–209

Delegate to the Continental Congress from South Carolina, served as its President 1777–78; Minister to Holland. While en route to his post he was captured and held prisoner in the Tower of London for fifteen months and was exchanged for Lord Cornwallis, 1781.

NEG. NO. 34616

JOHN MARSHALL
Richard N. Brooke, after W. D. Washington, 9' x 5'2''
Signed l.r. R. N. Brooke, Washington, 1880
Purchased 1881
House wing, third floor, west corridor

Chief Justice of the United States 1801–35; soldier in the Revolutionary
War; Member of Congress from Virginia and Secretary of State.

126

Ætatis suæ 21. Aº. 1616.

Matoaks als Rebecka daughter to the mighty Prince
Powhatan Emperour of Attanoughkomouck als Virginia
converted and baptized in the Christian faith, and
Wife to the Worll. Mr Tho: Rolff.

POCAHONTAS
Unknown artist, copy from original, 30″ x 25″
Gift of Henry S. Wellcome, 1899
Accepted by S. Res. of February 28, 1899, 55th Congress
S–233

American Indian princess; reputed to have saved Captain John Smith from execution; married to John Rolfe.

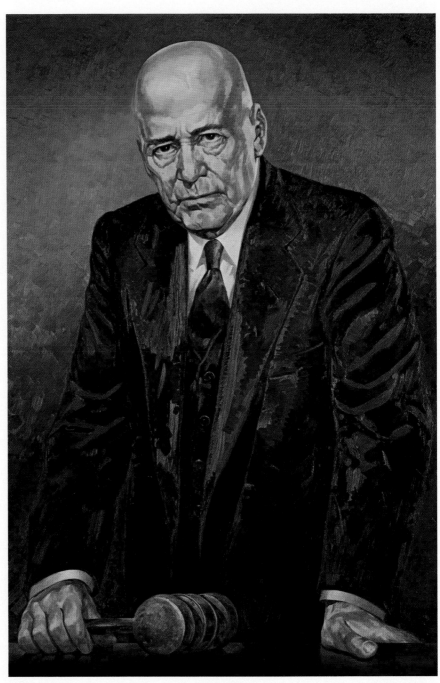

SAM RAYBURN
Signed l.r. Tom Lea, 1966; 59½″ x 39½″
Gift from Texas State Society, 1966
Accepted by House Office Building Commission, 1964
Rayburn House Office Building, east entrance

A Representative from Texas; Mr. Rayburn has the distinction of serving as Speaker of the House of Representatives longer than any other man.

Paintings

Rotunda
Senate Wing
House Wing
Central Section
Richard Brevard Russell Office Building
House Office Buildings

PAINTINGS IN THE ROTUNDA

EIGHT PAINTINGS

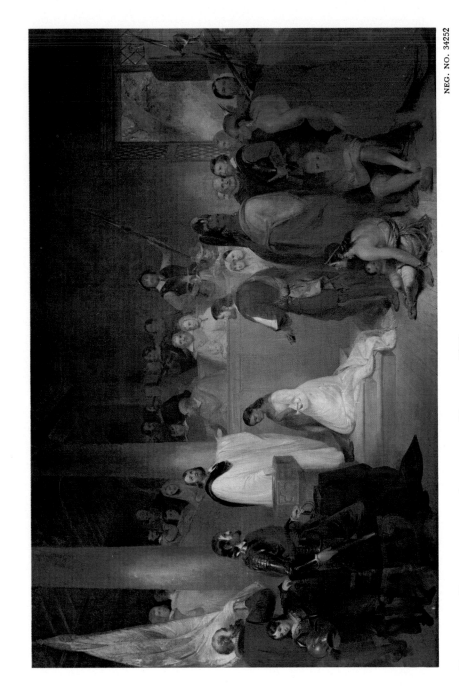

NEG. NO. 34252

Baptism of Pocahontas at Jamestown, Virginia, 1613
John G. Chapman, 12′ x 18′
Purchased; placed November 30, 1840

130

BAPTISM OF POCAHONTAS
At Jamestown Va. 1613

1. Pocahontas
2. John Rolfe
3. Alexander Whiteaker
4. Sir Thomas Dale
5. Sister of Pocahontas

6. Nantequaus, brother of Pocahontas
7. Opechancanough
8. Opachisco, uncle of Pocahontas
9. Richard Wyffin

10. Standard bearer
11. Mr. and Mrs. Forrest, the lady being the first gentlewoman to arrive in the colony

12. Henry Spilman
13. John and Anne Laydon, the first persons married in the colony
14. The page

131

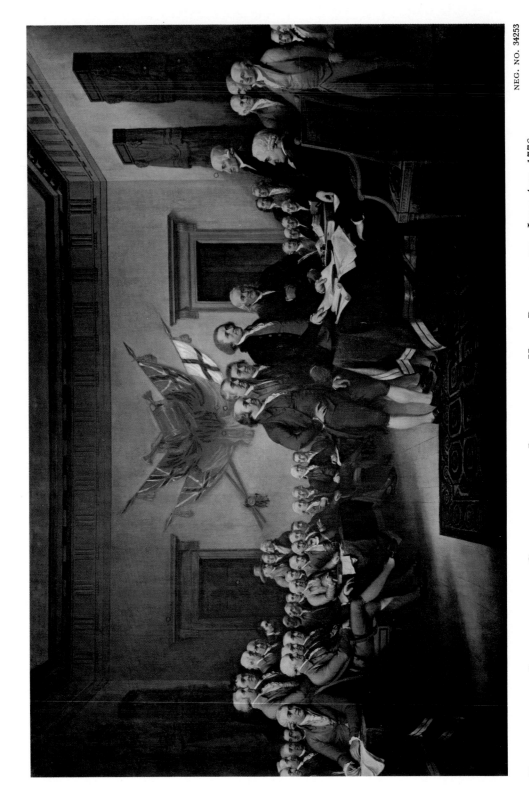

Declaration of Independence in Congress, at the Independence Hall, Philadelphia, July 4th, 1776
John Trumbull, 12' x 18'
Purchased March 4, 1819

132

DECLARATION OF INDEPENDENCE

In Congress, at the Independence Hall, Philadelphia, July 4th 1776.

1. George Wythe, Virginia
2. William Whipple, New Hampshire
3. Josiah Bartlett, New Hampshire
4. Benjamin Harrison, Virginia
5. Thomas Lynch, South Carolina
6. Richard Henry Lee, Virginia
7. Samuel Adams, Massachusetts
*8. George Clinton, New York
9. William Paca, Maryland
10. Samuel Chase, Maryland
11. Lewis Morris, New York
12. William Floyd, New York

13. Arthur Middleton, South Carolina
14. Thomas Heyward, Jr., South Carolina
15. Charles Carroll, Maryland
16. George Walton, Georgia
17. Robert Morris, Pennsylvania
*18. Thomas Willing, Pennsylvania
19. Benjamin Rush, Pennsylvania
20. Elbridge Gerry, Massachusetts
21. Robert Treat Paine, Massachusetts
22. Abraham Clark, New Jersey
23. Stephen Hopkins, Rhode Island
24. William Ellery, Rhode Island

25. George Clymer, Pennsylvania
26. William Hooper, North Carolina
27. Joseph Hewes, North Carolina
28. James Willson, Pennsylvania
29. Francis Hopkinson, New Jersey
30. John Adams, Massachusetts
31. Roger Sherman, Connecticut
*32. Robert R. Livingston, New York
33. Thomas Jefferson, Virginia
34. Benjamin Franklin, Pennsylvania
35. Richard Stockton, New Jersey
36. Francis Lewis, New York

37. John Witherspoon, New Jersey
38. Samuel Huntington, Connecticut
39. William Williams, Connecticut
40. Oliver Wolcott, Connecticut
41. John Hancock, Massachusetts
*42. Charles Thomson, Secretary, Pennsylvania
43. George Read, Delaware
*44. John Dickinson, Pennsylvania
45. Edward Rutledge, South Carolina
46. Thomas McKean, Delaware
47. Philip Livingston, New York

There were 56 signers of the Declaration of Independence. The painting portrays only 47. The 5 men whose names are starred were not signers. The portraits of the following 14 signers do not appear in the painting.

Matthew Thornton, New Hampshire
John Hart, New Jersey
John Morton, Pennsylvania
James Smith, Pennsylvania

George Taylor, Pennsylvania
George Ross, Pennsylvania
Caesar Rodney, Delaware
Thomas Stone, Maryland

Thomas Nelson, Jr., Virginia
Francis Lightfoot Lee, Virginia
Carter Braxton, Virginia
John Penn, North Carolina

Button Gwinnett, Georgia
Lyman Hall, Georgia

133

NEG. NO. 34254

DISCOVERY OF THE MISSISSIPPI BY DE SOTO A.D. 1541
William H. Powell, 12' x 18'
Signed l.r. W. H. Powell, 1853
Purchased; placed February 16, 1855

134

DE SOTO'S DISCOVERY OF THE MISSISSIPPI
A.D 1541

1. De Soto
2. Moorish servant
3. Confessor
4. Spanish cavalier

5. Artillerymen
6. Company of men planting a cross
7. Ecclesiastic bearing the censer

8. Priest blessing the cross
9. Soldier dressing his wounded leg
10. Camp chest with arms and helmets

11. Standard bearers and helmeted men
12. Two Indian maidens
13. Indian chiefs bearing the pipe of peace

Embarkation of the Pilgrims at Delft Haven, Holland, July 22nd, 1620
Signed l.l. Robt. W. Weir, 1843; 12' x 18'
Purchased; placed December 21, 1843

136

EMBARKATION OF THE PILGRIMS

At Delft Haven, Holland, July 22nd 1620.

1. Mr. Robinson, pastor of the congregation
2. Elder William Brewster
3. Mrs. Brewster and sick child
4. Governor Carver
5. William Bradford

6. Mr. and Mrs. White
7. Mr. and Mrs. Winslow
8. Mr. and Mrs. Fuller
9. Miles Standish and his wife Rose

10. Mrs. Bradford; she fell overboard the
    day the vessel came to anchor
11. Mrs. Carver and child
12. Captain Reynolds and sailor

13. Boy belonging to Carver and family
14. Boy in charge of Mr. Winslow
15. Boy belonging to Mrs. Winslow's family
16. A nurse and child

137

GENERAL GEORGE WASHINGTON RESIGNING HIS COMMISSION TO CONGRESS AS COMMANDER IN CHIEF OF THE ARMY
AT ANNAPOLIS, MARYLAND, DECEMBER 23D, 1783
John Trumbull, 12' x 18'
Purchased December 24, 1824

138

GEN. WASHINGTON RESIGNING HIS COMMISSION

to Congress at Annapolis Md. Decemb. 23ᵈ 1783

1. Thomas Mifflin, Pennsylvania, President
   Delegate
2. Charles Thompson, Pennsylvania
   Secretary
3. Elbridge Gerry, Massachusetts
   Delegate
4. Hugh Williamson, North Carolina
   Delegate
5. Samuel Osgood, Massachusetts
   Delegate
6. Eleazer McComb, Delaware
   Delegate
7. George Partridge, Massachusetts
   Delegate
8. Edward Lloyd, Maryland
   Delegate

9. Richard D. Spaight, North Carolina
   Delegate
10. Benjamin Hawkins, North Carolina
    Delegate
11. Abiel Foster, New Hampshire
    Delegate
12. Thomas Jefferson, Virginia
    Delegate
13. Arthur Lee, Virginia
    Delegate
14. David Howell, Rhode Island
    Delegate
15. James Monroe, Virginia
    Delegate
16. Jacob Read, South Carolina
    Delegate

17. James Madison, Virginia
    Spectator
18. William Ellery, Rhode Island
    Delegate
19. J. Townley Chase, Maryland
    Delegate
20. Samuel Hardy, Virginia
    Delegate
21. Charles Morris, Pennsylvania
    Delegate
22. General Washington
23. Col. Benjamin Walker
    Aide-de-camp
24. Col. David Humphreys
    Aide-de-camp

25. General Smallwood, Maryland
    Spectator
26. Gen. Otho Holland Williams, Maryland
    Spectator
27. Col. Samuel Smith, Maryland
    Spectator
28. Col. John E. Howard, Maryland
    Spectator
29. Charles Carroll and two daughters,
    Maryland
30. Mrs. Washington and her three grand-
    children
31. Daniel of St. Thomas Jenifer, Maryland
    Spectator

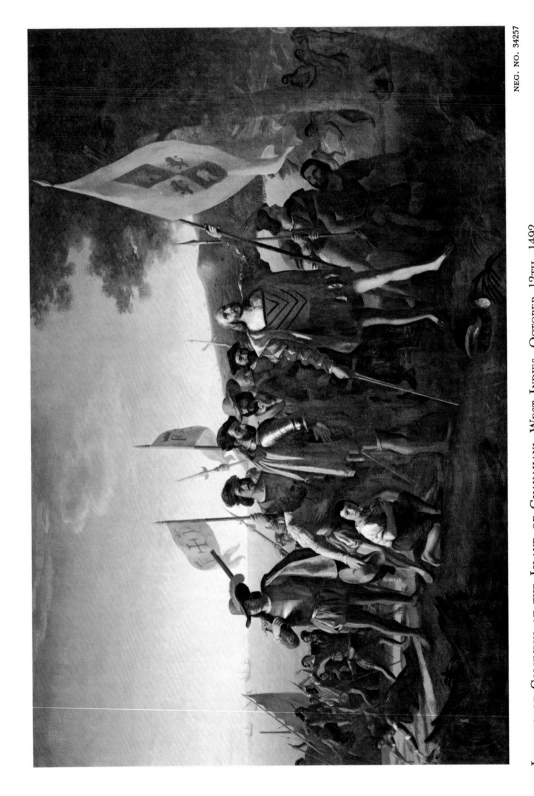

LANDING OF COLUMBUS AT THE ISLAND OF GUANAHANI, WEST INDIES, OCTOBER 12TH, 1492
John Vanderlyn, 12′ x 18′
Purchased; placed January 15, 1847

LANDING OF COLUMBUS

At the Island of Guanahani, West-Indies. October 12th 1492.

1. Columbus
2. Martin Alonzo Pinzon
3. Vincent Yannez Pinzon
4. Rodrigo des Escobedo or Escobar, notary of the armament
5. Roderigo Sanchez, inspector of armament
6. Mutineer in a suppliant attitude
7. Alonzo de Ojeda
8. Cabin boy
9. Soldier
10. Sailor
11. Friar bearing a crucifix

141

NEG. NO. 34258

SURRENDER OF GENERAL BURGOYNE AT SARATOGA, NEW YORK, OCTOBER 17TH, 1777
John Trumbull, 12' x 18'
Purchased May 1, 1822

142

SURRENDER OF GENERAL BURGOYNE
At Saratoga N Y October 17ᵗʰ 1777

1. Major Lithcow, Massachusetts
2. Colonel Cilly, New Hampshire
3. General Stark, New Hampshire
4. Captain Seymour, of Shelton's Horse
5. Major Hull, Massachusetts
6. Colonel Greaton, Massachusetts
7. Major Dearborne, New Hampshire
8. Colonel Scammell, New Hampshire
9. Colonel Lewis, Quartermaster General, New Hampshire

10. Major General Phillips, British
11. Lieutenant General Burgoyne, British
12. General Baron Riedesel, German
13. Colonel Wilkinson, Deputy Adjutant General, American
14. General Gates
15. Colonel Prescott, Massachusetts Volunteers

16. Colonel Morgan, Virginia Riflemen
17. Brig. Gen. Rufus Putnam, Massachusetts
18. Lieut. Col. John Brooks, late Governor of Massachusetts
19. Rev. Mr. Hitchcock, chaplain, Rhode Island
20. Maj. Rob Troup, Aide-de-camp, New York
21. Major Haskell

22. Major Armstrong
23. Maj. Gen. Philip Schuyler, Albany
24. Brigadier General Glover, Massachusetts
25. Brigadier General Whipple, New Hampshire Militia
26. Maj. M. Clarkson, Aide-de-camp, New York
27. Maj. Ebenezer Stevens, Massachusetts, commanding the artillery

143

SURRENDER OF LORD CORNWALLIS AT YORKTOWN, VIRGINIA, OCTOBER 19TH, 1781
John Trumbull, 12′ x 18′
Purchased November 13, 1820

144

SURRENDER OF LORD CORNWALLIS

At Yorktown Va. October 19th 1781.

The portraits of the French Officers were obtained in Paris 1787 and painted by Trumbull from the living part in the house of Jefferson then Minister to France from the United States.

1. Count Deuxponts
   Colonel of French Infantry
2. Duke de Laval Montmorency
   Colonel of French Infantry
3. Count Custine
   Colonel of French Infantry
4. Duke de Lauzun
   Colonel of French Cavalry
5. General Choizy
6. Viscount Viomenil
7. Marquis de St. Simon
8. Count Fersen
9. Count Charles Damas
   Aide-de-camp of Count Rochambeau
   Aide-de-camp of Count Rochambeau

10. Marquis Chastellux
11. Baron Viomenil
12. Count de Barras
    Admiral
13. Count de Grasse
    Admiral
14. Count Rochambeau
    General en Chef des Francais
15. General Lincoln
16. E. Stevens
    Colonel of American Artillery
17. General Washington
    Commander in Chief

18. Thomas Nelson
    Governor of Virginia
19. Marquis Lafayette
20. Baron Steuben
21. Colonel Cobb
    Aide-de-camp to General Washington
22. Colonel Trumbull
    Secretary to General Washington
23. Maj. Gen. James Clinton, New York
24. General Gist, Maryland
25. Gen. Anthony Wayne, Pennsylvania
26. General Hand, Pennsylvania
    Adjutant General
27. Gen. Peter Muhlenberg, Pennsylvania

28. Maj. Gen. Henry Knox
    Commander of Artillery
29. Lieut. Col. E. Huntington
    Acting Aide-de-camp of General Lincoln
30. Col. Timothy Pickering
    Quartermaster General
31. Col. Alexander Hamilton
    commanding Light Infantry
32. Col. John Laurens, South Carolina
33. Col. Walter Stuart, Philadelphia
34. Col. Nicholas Fish, New York

145

PAINTINGS IN THE SENATE WING

TWELVE PAINTINGS

BATTLE OF CHAPULTEPEC (STORMING OF CHAPULTEPEC)
James Walker, 17'6'' x 7'9½''
Purchased 1857–1862
In storage

BATTLE OF FORT MOULTRIE
John Blake White, 1815, 32″ x 50″
Gift of Dr. Octavius A. White, 1901
Accepted by the Joint Committee on the Library
Senate wing, third floor, south corridor

147

Battle of Lake Erie
William H. Powell, 20′ x 30′
Signed 1.1 W. H. Powell. 1873
Purchased 1865
Senate wing, east staircase

ELECTORAL COMMISSION OF 1877 (FLORIDA CASE)
Cornelia A. Fassett, 61½'' x 75''
Signed l.r. C. A. Fassett, 1879
Purchased 1886
Senate wing, third floor, east corridor

149

THE ELECTORAL COMMISSION OF 1877 (THE FLORIDA CASE)

IN THE GALLERY.

(The Press.)

1. W. H ROBERTS, New Orleans Times.
2. JOHN M. CARSON, New York Journal
3. BEN. PERLEY POORE, Boston Journal
4. GEORGE W. ADAMS, New York World.
5. T. C. CRAWFORD, Chicago Times.
6. A. M. GIBSON, New York Sun.
7. W. SCOTT SMITH, New York Evening Post.
8. C. W. FITCH, Pittsburgh Chronicle.
9. H. V. BOYNTON, Cincinnati Gazette.
10. WILSON J. VANCE, Cincinnati Commercial.
11. Mrs. JANE G. SWISSHELM.
12. L. A. GOBRIGHT, N.Y. Associated Press.
13. Mrs. S. J. LIPPINCOTT, ("Grace Greenwood,") N.Y. Times.
14. Miss AUSTINE SNEAD, ("Miss Grundy,") N.Y. Graphic.
15. Miss EMMA JANES, Toledo Blade, &c.
16. Mrs. MARY E. NEALY, Home Journal.
17. Mrs. M. D. LINCOLN, ("Bessie Beech,") Cleveland Plain-dealer.
18. Miss SALLIE WOODBURY, ("Ruby Wood,") National Union.
19. Mrs. FANNIE B. WARD, New Orleans Picayune.
20. Mrs. ADELE M. GARRIGUES, Courier, East Saginaw, Mich.
21. W. M. OLIN, Boston Advertiser.
22. W. O. FISHBACK, St. Louis Republican.
23. DeB. R. KEIM, Philadelphia Press.
24. CROSBY S. NOYES, Ed. Evening Star, Washington, D.C.
25. JAMES R. YOUNG, Philadelphia Evening Star.
26. W. E. CURTIS, Chicago Inter-Ocean.
27. E. B. WIGHT, Chicago Tribune.
28. E. H. LUTHER. Boston Post.
29. CHARLES NORDHOFF, New York Herald.
30. CLIFFORD WARDEN, Pittsburgh Telegraph.
31. F. A. RICHARDSON, Baltimore Sun.
32. E. V. SMALLEY, New York Tribune.
33. L. WASHINGTON, Louisville Courier-Journal.
34. Mrs. E. S. CROMWELL, Chicago Herald.
35. Mrs. NELLIE S. STOWELL, Kansas City Journal.
36. Mrs. FAYETTA C. SNEAD, ("Fay,") Louisville Courier-Journal.
37. Mrs. A. ROWLAND, Oxford (Pa.) Press.
38. FRANK HATTON, Ed. Burlington Hawkeye.
39. E. STODDARDT JOHNSON, Ed. Frankfort Yeoman.
40. A. C. BUELL, The Capital.
41. Mrs. A. D. JOHNSTON, Rochester Democrat and Chronicle.
42. Miss MARY E. MANN, Troy Daily Times.
43. CHARLES L. FLANAGAN, Philadelphia North American.
44. Mrs. ELVIRA BLISS SHELDON, ("Aunt True,") Grand Rapids Eagle.
45. W. HARRY CLARKE, National Associated Press.
46. I. N. BURRITT, Ed. Washington Herald.
47. C. CATHCART TAYLOR, Philadelphia Times.
48. WM. P. COPELAND, New York Commercial Bulletin.
49. E. F. WATERS, Prop. Boston Advertiser.
50. J. EDWARDS CLARKE, New York Mail.
51. JNO. C. BURCH, Ed. Nashville American.
52. Mr. GODDARD, Ed. Boston Advertiser.
53. HOWARD CARROL, New York Times.
54. S. H. KAUFFMANN, Evening Star.
55. WM. C. MAC BRIDE, Cincinnati Enquirer.
56. Z. L. WHITE, New York Tribune.
57. EDWIN FLEMING, N.Y. Journal of Commerce.
58. L. W. KENNEDY, Daily Chronicle, Washington, D.C.
59. J. DEE, Detroit Evening News.
60. GEORGE DOUGLAS, Washington Capital.
61. Mr. PARR, Pittsburgh Post.
62. Mrs. G. W. THOMSON, Journal.

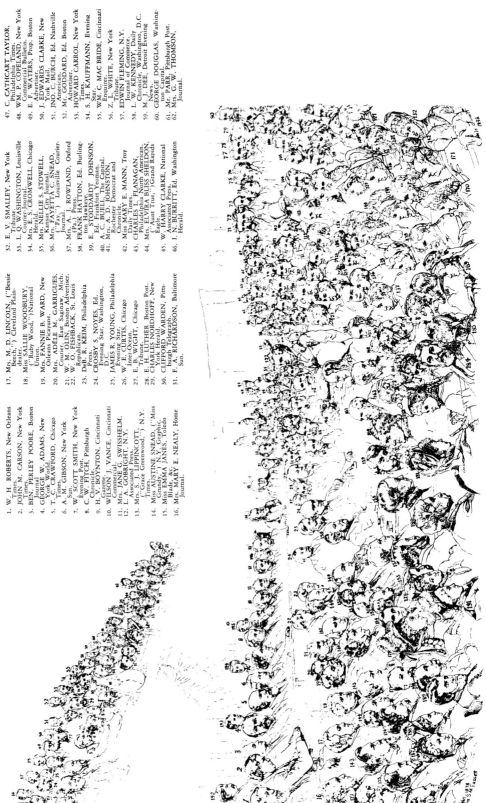

17. WILLIAM WINDOM, Senator, Minnesota.
18. W. W. CORCORAN.
19. JOHN J. INGALLS, Senator, Kansas.
20. J. C. S. BLACKBURN, Member of Congress, Kentucky.
21. JOHN H. REAGAN, Member of Congress, Texas.
22. B. E. CATTIN, Assistant Secretary Electoral Com.
23. GEORGE A. HOWARD, Assistant Secretary Electoral Com.
24. JAMES H. McKENNEY, Secretary Electoral Commission.
25. JOHN SHERMAN, Senator, Ohio.
26. SAMUEL SHELLABARGER, Counsel for Hayes.
27. WILLIAM F. COOPER, Page to Electoral Commission.
28. D. F. MURPHY, Stenographer Electoral Commission.
29. GEORGE W. McCRARY, M. C., Ia., and counsel for Hayes.
30. MORRISON R. WAITE, Chief Justice, U.S.S.C.
31. JOHN G. THOMPSON, Sergeant-at-Arms, H.R.
32. JOHN J. NICOLAY, Marshall, U.S.S.C.
33. W. H. REARDON, Marshall, Electoral Commission.
34. E. P. CORVAIZIER, Messenger, U.S. Senate.
35. MRS. Z. CHANDLER.
36. MISS G. A. BOUTWELL.
37. JOHN R. FRENCH, Sergeant-at-Arms, U.S. Senate.
38. MISS G. F. TUCKER.
39. MRS. CHARLES E. HOOKER.
40. MISS CAROLINE BRADLEY.
41.
42. MISS LIDA MILLER.
43. MISS JULIA D. STRONG.
44. PROF. JOSEPH HENRY, Smithsonian Institution.
45. CHARLES G. WILLIAMS, Member of Congress, Wisconsin.
46. MRS. S. VIRGINIA FIELD.
47. MRS. MARY A. MATTHEWS.
48. MRS. RUTH A. HOAR.
49. MRS. CHAPMAN COLEMAN.
50. HAMILTON FISH, Secretary of State.
51. MRS. JULIA K. FISH.
52. MRS. MYRA CLARK GAINES.
53. MRS. JULIA G. TYLER, (Widow of Ex-President Tyler.)
54. MRS. I. V. SWEARINGEN.
55. MRS. VIRGINIA M. WILSON.
56. MRS. RACHAEL H. STRONG.
57. CHARLES GORDON.
58. MRS. IMOGENE M. MORRELL.
59. MRS. JEAN M. LANDER.
60. MISS KATHERINE LEE BAYARD.
61. JOHN J. PATTERSON, Senator, South Carolina.
62. MRS. CATHERINE HARDENBERGH.
63. JOHN H. FLAGG, Legislative Clerk, U.S. Senate.
64. JOHN HITZ, Consul General of Switzerland.
65. CHARLES PAGE BRYAN.
66. GEORGE M. ADAMS, Clerk, House of Representatives.
67. HORATIO KING.
68. S. W. DORSEY, Senator, Arkansas.
69. M. B. BRADY.
70. AMBROSE E. BURNSIDE, Senator, Rhode Island.
71. GEORGE C. GORHAM, Secretary, U.S. Senate.
72. SAMUEL J. RANDALL, Speaker, House of Representatives.
73. F. M. COCKRELL, Senator, Missouri.
74. J. PROCTOR KNOTT, Member of Congress, Kentucky.
75. JOHN B. CLARK, Jr., Member of Congress, Missouri.
76. H. B. ANTHONY, Senator, Rhode Island.
77. BAINBRIDGE WADLEIGH, Senator, New Hampshire.
78. BENJAMIN H. HILL, Senator, Georgia.
79. FERNANDO WOOD, Member of Congress, New York.
80. A. C. HARMER, Member of Congress, Pa.
81. ANNANIAS HERBERT, Messenger, U.S. Supreme Court.
82. G. A. CLARK, Doorkeeper, U.S. Supreme Court.
83. AUGUSTUS W. CUTLER, Member of Congress, New Jersey.
84. A. R. SHEPHERD.
85. S. L. PHELPS, Commissioner, District of Columbia.
86. J. W. POWELL, United States Survey.
87. S. A. HURLBUT, M. C., Ill., and counsel for Hayes.
88. JOHN J. KASSON, M. C., Ia., and counsel for Hayes.
89. GEORGE W. CHILDS.
90. JAMES L. ANDEM, Reporter for N.Y. Asso. Press.
91. STANLEY MATTHEWS, Counsel for Hayes.
92. MRS. J. A. GARFIELD.
93. GEORGE M. ROBESON, Secretary of War.
94. ALPHONSO M. TAFT, Secretary of War.
95. BELVA M. LOCKWOOD.
96. GEORGE S. BOUTWELL, Senator, Massachusetts.
97. AARON A. SARGENT, Senator, California.
98. DR. PETER PARKER.
99. JAMES O. WOODRUFF, Scientific Expedition.
100. EUGENE HALE, Member of Congress, Maine.
101. CHARLES FOSTER, Member of Congress, Ohio.
102. JOHN H. MITCHELL, Senator, Oregon.
103. W. P. LYNDE, Member of Congress, Wisconsin.
104. JOHN D. C. ATKINS, Member of Congress, Tennessee.
105. A. A. HARDENBERGH, Member of Congress, New Jersey.
106. THOMAS EWING, Member of Congress, Ohio.
107. WILLIAM E. CHANDLER, Counsel for Hayes.
108. JAMES P. ROOT, Counsel for Hayes.
109. JAMES N. TYNER, Postmaster General.
110. WILLIAM LAWRENCE, M. C., Ohio, counsel for Hayes.
111. D. T. CORBIN.
112. C. D. DRAKE, Chief Justice, U.S. C. of Claims.
113. CHARLES W. JONES, Senator, Florida.
114. P. PHILLIPS.
115. SAUNDERS W. JOHNSTON.
116. N. P. BANKS, Member of Congress, Massachusetts.
117. J. G. CANNON, Member of Congress, Illinois.
118. FLORA FASSETT.
119. ELIZABETH B. JOHNSTON.
120. W. A. J. SPARKS, Member of Congress, Illinois.
121. FREDERICK DOUGLASS.
122. WILLIAM M. EVARTS, Counsel for Hayes.
123. EDWIN W. STOUGHTON, Counsel for Hayes.
124. ZACHARIAH CHANDLER, Secretary of the Interior.
125. ABRAM S. HEWITT, Member of Congress, New York.
126. AMERICUS V. RICE, Member of Congress, Ohio.
127. MRS. CELIA S. SHERMAN.
128. MRS. JENNIE B. BRYAN.
129. MRS. SUSAN M. EDMUNDS.
130. MRS. E. V. MILLER.
131. WILLIAM D. KELLEY, Member of Congress, Pennsylvania.
132. MRS. MARY CLEMMER.
133. CHARLES O'CONOR, Counsel for Tilden.
134. RICHARD T. MERRICK, Counsel for Tilden.
135. GEORGE A. JENKS, M. C., Pa., and counsel for Tilden.
136. W. H. FORNEY, Member of Congress, Alabama.
137. J. RANDOLPH TUCKER, M. C., Va., and counsel for Tilden.
138. TIMOTHY O. HOWE, Sen., Wis., and counsel for Hayes.
139. HENRY WATTERSON, Member of Congress, Kentucky.
140. MRS. ELLEN F. WINDOM.
141. THOMAS B. BRYAN.
142. HIRAM P. BELL, Member of Congress, Georgia.
143. L. Q. C. LAMAR, Member of Congress, Mississippi.
144. HANNIBAL HAMLIN, Senator, Maine.
145. GEORGE BANCROFT, Historian.
146. JUSTIN S. MORRILL, Senator, Vermont.
147. JOHN A. CAMPBELL, Counsel for Tilden.
148. ROSCOE CONKLING, Senator, New York.
149. MONTGOMERY BLAIR, Counsel for Tilden.
150. MATT W. RANSOM, Senator, North Carolina.
151. DAVID DUDLEY FIELD, M. C., N.Y., counsel for Tilden.
152. WILLIAM C. WHITNEY, Counsel for Tilden.
153. THOMAS W. FERRY, President pro Tempore, U.S. Senate.
154. JAMES H. BLOUNT, Member of Congress, Georgia.
155. J. D. CAMERON, Senator, Pennsylvania.
156. MARTIN I. TOWNSEND, Member of Congress, New York.
157. WILLIAM M. SPRINGER, Member of Congress, Illinois.
158. LYMAN TRUMBULL, Counsel for Tilden.
159. MATT H. CARPENTER, Counsel for Tilden.
160. JEREMIAH S. BLACK, Counsel for Tilden.
161. GEORGE HOADLY, Counsel for Tilden.
162. ASHABEL GREEN, Counsel for Tilden.
163. MATTHEW G. EMERY.
164. ALEX. PORTER MORSE, Counsel for Tilden.
165. H. B. BANNING, Member of Congress, Ohio.
166. MRS. NANNIE MERRICK.
167. BLANCHE K. BRUCE, Senator, Mississippi.
168. HENRY W. BLAIR, Member of Congress, New Hampshire.
169. MISS M. Y. FRELINGHUYSEN.
170. MRS. CHRISTINE TYNER.
171. SIR EDWARD THORNTON, British Minister.
172. HIESTER CLYMER, Member of Congress, Pennsylvania.
173. MRS. LAURA H. TUCKER.
174. MRS. FANNIE H. GORDON.
175. JOHN B. GORDON, Senator, Georgia.
176. JOHN A. LOGAN, Senator, Illinois.
177. S. S. COX, Member of Congress, New York.
178. MARY F. WAITE.
179. MRS. HELEN M. DORSEY.
180. THOMAS SWAN, Member of Congress, Maryland.
181. MRS. MARY CAMERON.
182. MRS. C. ADELE FASSETT.
183. MRS. MARY A. RICE.
184. JAMES G. BLAINE, Senator, Maine.
185. MRS. SALLIE R. KNOTT.
186. CARLILE P. PATTERSON, Superintendent U.S. Coast Survey.
187. MRS. C. P. PATTERSON.
188. MRS. MARY M. GIBSON.
189. W. B. ALLISON, Senator, Iowa.
190. RANDALL LEE GIBSON, Member of Congress, Louisiana.
191. MRS. LILLIE E. WILLIS.
192. CHARLES W. HOFFMAN, Librarian of Law Library, U.S.S.C.
193. C. H. McCALL, Page, Supreme Court U.S.
194. ROBERT BROWN, Page, Supreme Court U.S.
195. FRED W. MATTESON, Page, Supreme Court U.S.
196. H. J. LAUCK, Messenger, Electoral Commission.

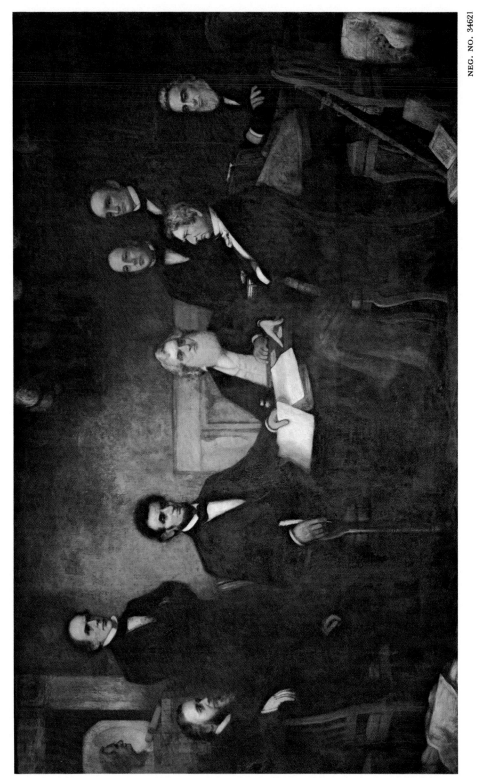

First Reading of the Emancipation Proclamation
Francis Bicknell Carpenter, 1864, 9' x 14' 6''
Gift of Mrs. Elizabeth Thompson, 1878
Accepted by Public Res. 6, 45th Congress
Senate wing, west staircase

152

THE FIRST READING OF THE EMANCIPATION PROCLAMATION

1. Abraham Lincoln
   President
2. William H. Seward
   Secretary of State

3. Salmon P. Chase
   Secretary of Treasury
4. Edwin M. Stanton
   Secretary of War

5. Edward Bates
   Attorney General
6. Montgomery Blair
   Postmaster General

7. Gideon Welles
   Secretary of Navy
8. Caleb B. Smith
   Secretary of Interior

153

General Marion Inviting a British Officer to Share His Meal
John Blake White, about 1810–1815, 24½″ x 29½″
Gift of Dr. Octavius A. White, 1899
Accepted by Senate Res. 510, 55th Congress
Senate wing, third floor, south corridor

LEIV EIRIKSSON DISCOVERS AMERICA, A.D. 1000
Per Krohg, after Christian Krohg, 5'5½'' x 8'4''
Signed l.r. efter C. Krohg 1893, ved P. Krohg 1936
Gift of Norwegian friends of America through
  Dr. Alf Bjercke of Oslo, Norway, 1936
Accepted by Public Res. 78, 74th Congress
Senate wing, third floor, east corridor

155

Mrs. Motte Directing Generals Marion and Lee to Burn Her Mansion to Dislodge the British

John Blake White, about 1810–1815, 24½″ x 29½″
Gift of Dr. Octavius A. White, 1899
Accepted by Senate Res. 510, 55th Congress
Senate wing, third floor, south corridor

156

NEG. NO. 24475

NIAGARA FALLS IN WINTER
Regis Gignoux, 1848, 52″ x 36″
Signed l.r. R. Gignoux
Gift of Mrs. Charles Carroll of Doughoregan Manor, Maryland
Accepted by the Joint Committee on the Library, 1901
Senate wing, third floor, south corridor

NEG. NO. 34626

RECALL OF COLUMBUS
Augustus G. Heaton, 51″ x 91″
Signed l.r. Copyright 1891 by A. G. Heaton, 1882
Purchased 1883
Senate wing, third floor, east corridor

158

SERGEANTS JASPER AND NEWTON RESCUING AMERICAN PRISONERS FROM THE BRITISH
John Blake White, about 1810–1815, 24½″ x 29½″
Gift of Dr. Octavius A. White, 1899
Accepted by Senate Res. 510, 55th Congress
Senate wing, third floor, south corridor

WE (LINDBERGH'S FLIGHT)
Einar Kverne, 1927, 36″ x 50″
Gift of Robert W. Woodruff, 1928
Accepted by the Joint Committee on the Library
Location unknown. No Photograph

PAINTINGS IN THE HOUSE WING

FIVE PAINTINGS

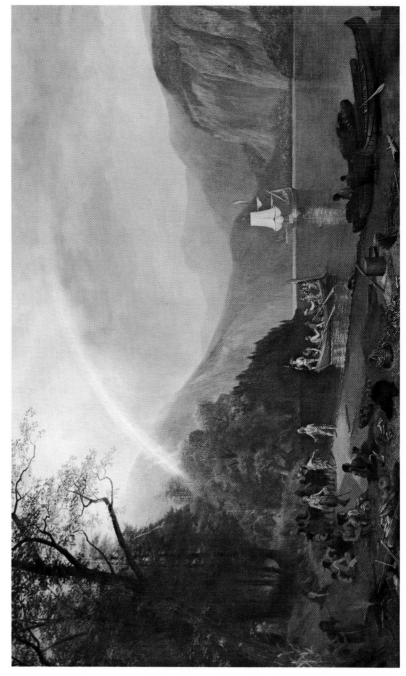

NEG. NO. 34628

DISCOVERY OF THE HUDSON RIVER
Albert Bierstadt, 6' x 10'
Signed l.r. A. Bierstadt
Purchased 1875
Members' private stairway, east corridor

160

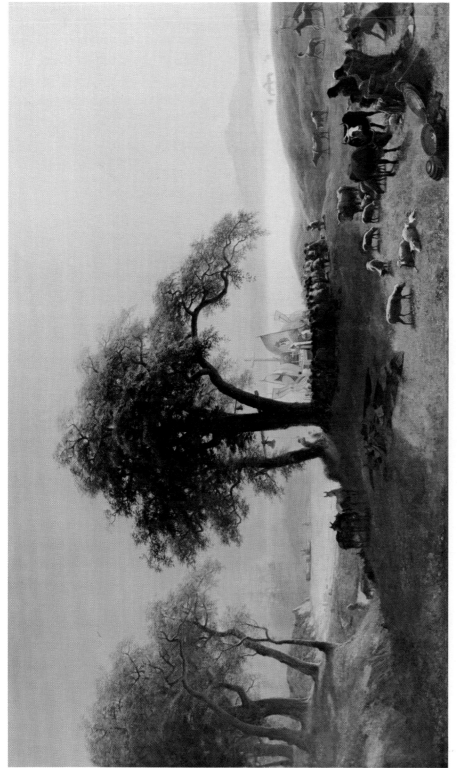

ENTRANCE INTO MONTEREY
Albert Bierstadt, 6' x 10'
Signed l.r. A. Bierstadt
Purchased 1878
Members' private stairway, west corridor

161

SCENE AT THE SIGNING OF THE CONSTITUTION OF THE UNITED STATES
Signed l.r. Howard Chandler Christy, Sail Loft, U.S. Navy Yard, Washington, D.C., April 1940; 20' x 30'
Purchased 1940 by Public Res. 11, 76th Congress
House wing, east stairway

162

SCENE AT THE SIGNING OF THE CONSTITUTION OF THE UNITED STATES

1. Washington, George, Va.
2. Franklin, Benjamin, Pa.
3. Madison, James, Va.
4. Hamilton, Alexander, N.Y.
5. Morris, Gouverneur, Pa.
6. Morris, Robert, Pa.
7. Wilson, James, Pa.
8. Pinckney, Chas. Cotesworth, S.C.
9. Pinckney, Chas, S.C.
10. Rutledge, John, S.C.
11. Butler, Pierce, S.C.
12. Sherman, Roger, Conn.
13. Johnson, William Samuel, Conn.
14. McHenry, James, Md.
15. Read, George, Del.
16. Bassett, Richard, Del.
17. Spaight, Richard Dobbs, N.C.
18. Blount, William, N.C.
19. Williamson, Hugh, N.C.
20. Jenifer, Daniel of St. Thomas, Md.
21. King, Rufus, Mass.
22. Gorham, Nathaniel, Mass.
23. Dayton, Jonathan, N.J.
24. Carroll, Daniel, Md.
25. Few, William, Ga.
26. Baldwin, Abraham, Ga.
27. Langdon, John, N.H.
28. Gilman, Nicholas, N.H.
29. Livingston, William, N.J.
30. Paterson, William, N.J.
31. Mifflin, Thomas, Pa.
32. Clymer, George, Pa.
33. FitzSimons, Thomas, Pa.
34. Ingersoll, Jared, Pa.
35. Bedford, Gunning, Jr., Del.
36. Brearley, David, N.J.
37. Dickinson, John, Del.
38. Blair, John, Va.
39. Broom, Jacob, Del.
40. Jackson, William, Secretary

UNITED STATES CAPITOL, East Front
Signed l.r. Paul N. Norton; 1971, watercolor, 28½″ x 21″
Gift of the U.S. Capitol Historical Society, 1971
Accepted by the Joint Committee on the Library
H–107

WESTWARD THE COURSE OF EMPIRE TAKES ITS WAY
Signed l.l. Painted by Emanuel Leutze 1862; fresco, 20' x 30'
Commissioned 1861
House wing, west stairway

PAINTINGS IN THE CENTRAL SECTION

EIGHTEEN PAINTINGS

LANDING OF COLUMBUS IN SAN SALVADOR
Signed 1.1. Boris Plenkovich N.A., 1966; 31½″ x 39″
Gift from the National Columbus Day Committee, 1966
Accepted by the Joint Committee on the Library
In storage. Not illustrated

Seventeen paintings of historic forts by Brigadier General Seth Eastman all hang in the center building, first floor, west corridor. General Eastman, working under special orders from the President, depicted the principal fortifications of the United States. The paintings were executed between 1870 and the time of his death in 1875. The date is given if it appears on the canvas.
This collection includes:

Fort Defiance, New Mexico (now Arizona)	Fort Snelling, Minnesota
Fort Delaware, Delaware	Fort Sumter, South Carolina (before the war)
Fort Jefferson, Florida	Fort Sumter, South Carolina (after the bombardment)
Fort Knox, Maine	
Fort Lafayette, New York	Fort Sumter, South Carolina (after the war)
Fort Mackinac, Michigan	Fort Taylor, Florida
Fort Mifflin, Pennsylvania	Fort Tompkins and Fort Wadsworth, New York
Fort Rice, North Dakota	Fort Trumbull, Connecticut
Fort Scammel and Fort Gorges, Maine	Fort West Point, New York

NEG. NO. 24110

FORT DEFIANCE, New Mexico (now Arizona)
Seth Eastman, 21½″ x 31½″
Signed bottom l. center S. E., 1873
Center section, first floor, west corridor

167

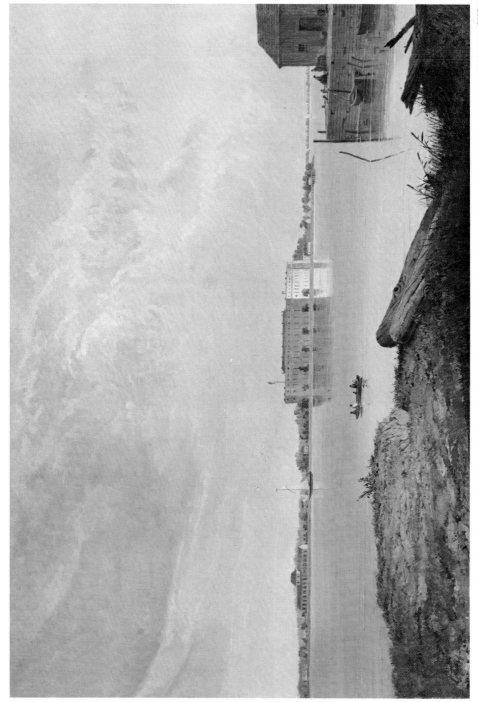

Fort Delaware, Delaware
Seth Eastman, 24½″ x 35½″
Signed l.l. S. E.
Center section, first floor, west corridor

168

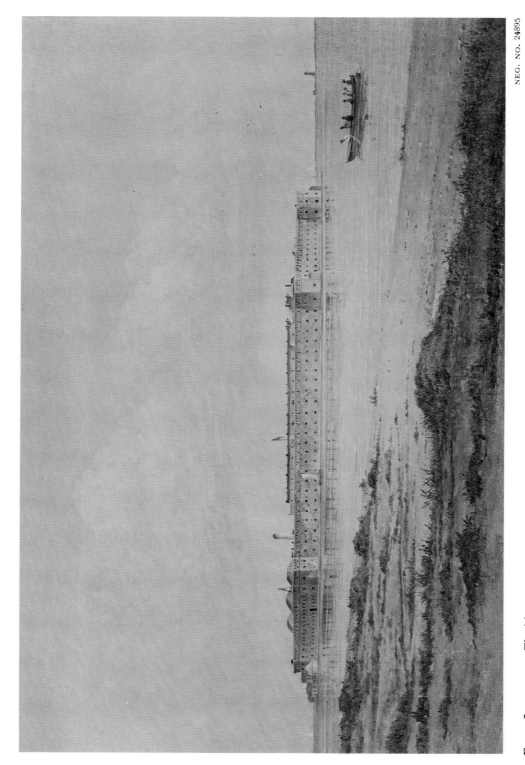

NEG. NO. 24895

FORT JEFFERSON, Florida
Seth Eastman, 1875; 21½″ x 31½″
Center section, first floor, west corridor

FORT KNOX, Maine
Seth Eastman, 24½″ x 35½″
Center section, first floor, west corridor

NEG. NO. 24896

170

NEG. NO. 24109

FORT LAFAYETTE, New York
Seth Eastman, 24½″ x 35½″
Signed l.l. S. E.
Center section, first floor, west corridor

171

FORT MACKINAC, Michigan
Seth Eastman, 24½″ x 35½″
Signed l.r. S. E., 1872
Center section, first floor, west corridor

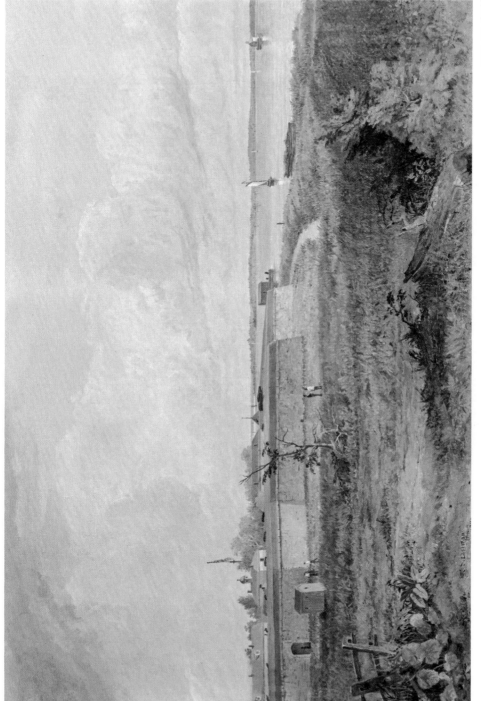

FORT MIFFLIN, Pennsylvania
Seth Eastman, 21½″ x 31½″
Signed l.l. S. Eastman, U.S.A., 1873
Center section, first floor, west corridor

173

FORT RICE, North Dakota
Seth Eastman, 21½″ x 31½″
Signed l.r. S. E., 1873
Center section, first floor, west corridor

FORT SCAMMEL AND FORT GORGES, Maine
Seth Eastman, 24½″ x 35½″
Signed l.r. S. E., 1872
Center section, first floor, west corridor

175

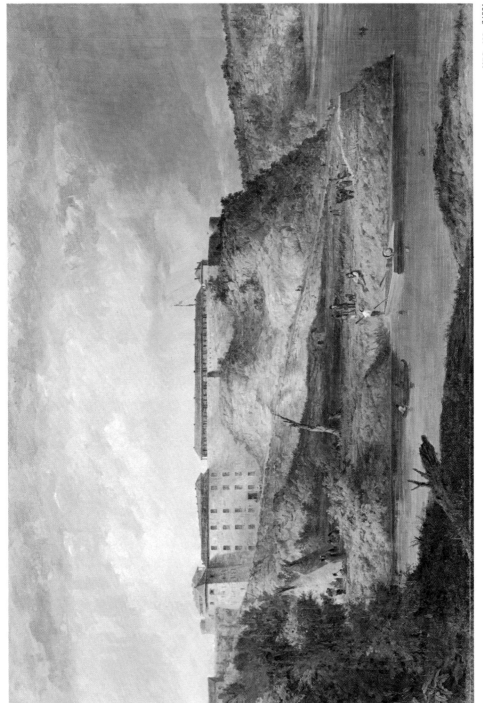

FORT SNELLING, Minnesota
Seth Eastman, 24½″ x 35½″
Signed l.r. S. Eastman
Center section, first floor, west corridor

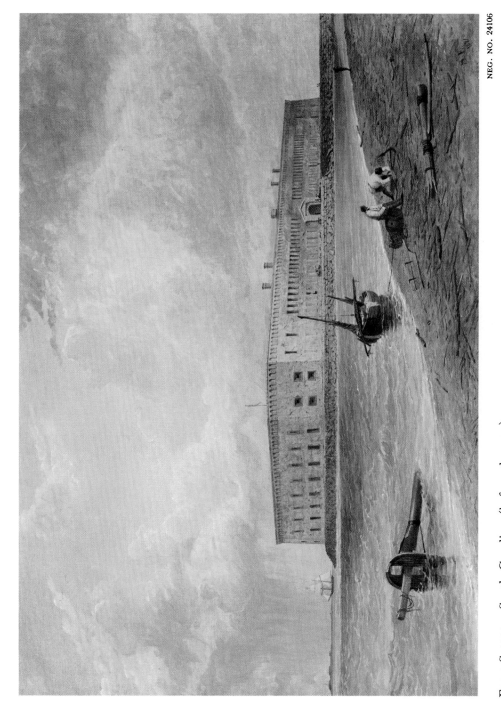

FORT SUMTER, South Carolina (before the war)
Seth Eastman, 24½″ x 35½″
Signed l.r. S. E., 1871
Center section, first floor, west corridor

177

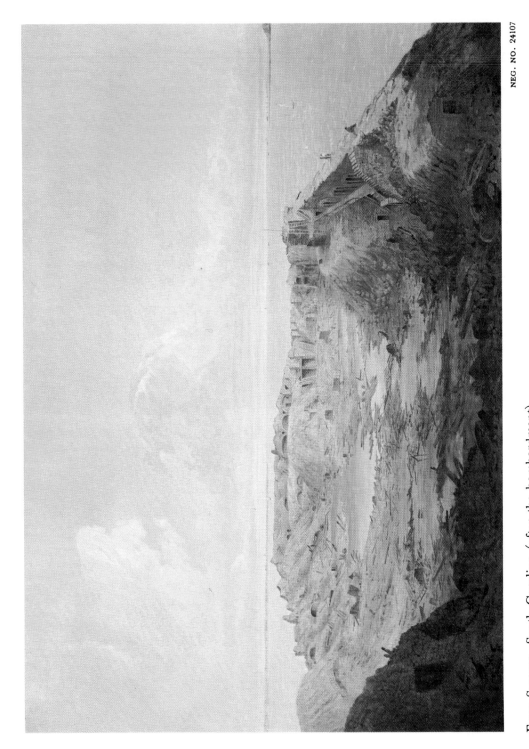

Fort Sumter, South Carolina (after the bombardment)
Seth Eastman, 24½″ x 35½″
Center section, first floor, west corridor

178

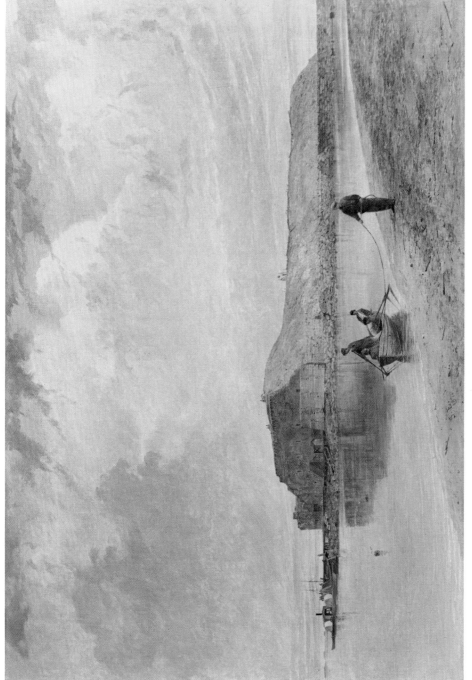

FORT SUMTER, South Carolina (after the war)
Seth Eastman, 24½″ x 35½″
Signed bottom l. center S. E., 1870
Center section, first floor, west corridor

179

FORT TAYLOR, Florida
Seth Eastman, 21½″ x 31½″
Center section, first floor, west corridor

NEG. NO. 24902

FORT TOMPKINS AND FORT WADSWORTH, New York
Seth Eastman, 24½″ x 35½″
Signed bottom l. center S. E.
Center section, first floor, west corridor

NEG. NO. 24105

FORT TRUMBULL, Connecticut
Seth Eastman, 24½" x 35½"
Center section, first floor, west corridor

182

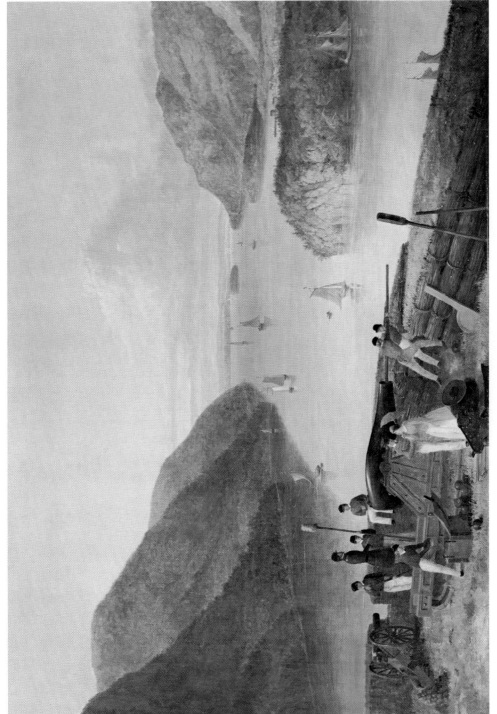

FORT WEST POINT, New York
Seth Eastman, 24½″ x 35½″
Center section, first floor, west corridor

PAINTING IN THE RICHARD BREVARD RUSSELL OFFICE BUILDING

ONE PAINTING

BRIDES OF VENICE
J. H. Van Lerius, 8′ 1′′ x 4′ ¾′′
Gift of daughters of Mrs. Alice Pike Barney, 1934
Accepted by the Joint Committee on the Library
In storage. Not illustrated

PAINTINGS IN THE HOUSE OFFICE BUILDINGS

TEN PAINTINGS

Nine paintings of Indian scenes were executed by Brigadier General Seth Eastman between 1867 and 1869 under a special commission directing him to decorate the House Indian Affairs Committee room in the Capitol. In 1945 the committee (renamed Interior and Insular Affairs in 1951) moved to the Longworth House Office Building, room 1324, and the collection was hung there. The date of painting is given if it appears on the canvas.
The scenes represented are:

Buffalo Chase
Death Whoop
Dog Dance of the Dakotas
Feeding the Dead
Indian Council

Indian Mode of Traveling
Indian Woman Dressing a Deer Skin
Rice Gatherers
Spearing Fish in Winter

The marine painting, "Peace," represents the White Squadron as constituted in 1891, lying peacefully at anchor. This squadron was the nucleus of the modern U.S. Navy fleet.

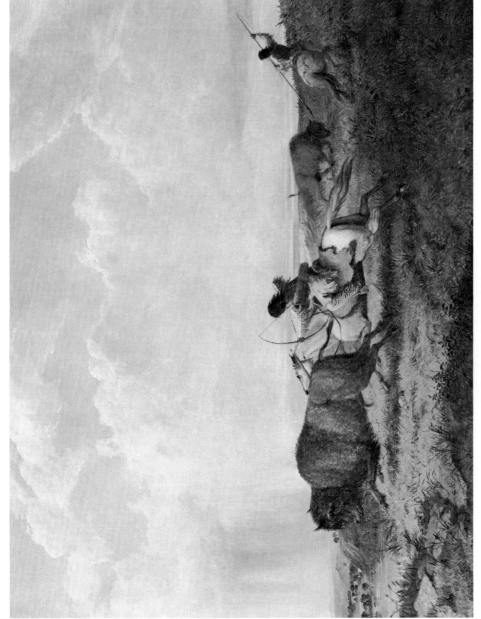

BUFFALO CHASE
Seth Eastman, 24″ x 31½″
Signed l.l. S. E. 1868
1324 Longworth House Office Building

185

DEATH WHOOP
Seth Eastman, 38½″ x 28″
Signed l.r. S. E. 1868
1324 Longworth House Office Building

Dog Dance of the Dakotas
Seth Eastman, 31″ x 44″
Signed l.r. S. E. 1868
1324 Longworth House Office Building

NEG. NO. 34111

FEEDING THE DEAD
Seth Eastman, 24″ x 31½″
Signed l.r. S. E. 1868
1324 Longworth House Office Building

188

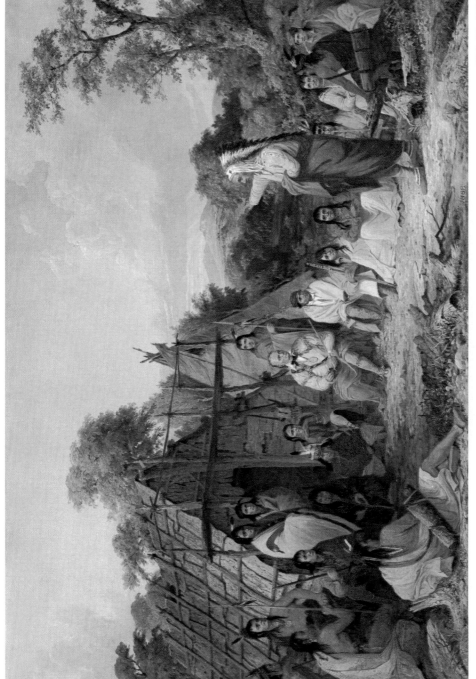

NEG. NO. 34112

INDIAN COUNCIL
Seth Eastman, 31″ x 44″
Signed l.r. S. E. 1868
1324 Longworth House Office Building

189

INDIAN MODE OF TRAVELING
Seth Eastman, 31″ x 44″
Signed l.l. S. E. 1869
1324 Longworth House Office Building

NEG. NO. 34113

190

INDIAN WOMAN DRESSING A DEER SKIN
Seth Eastman, 38½″ x 28″
1324 Longworth House Office Building

NEG. NO. 34115

RICE GATHERERS
Seth Eastman, 31½″ x 40½″
Signed l.l. S. E. 1867
1324 Longworth House Office Building

192

SPEARING FISH IN WINTER
Seth Eastman, 31″ x 44″
1324 Longworth House Office Building

NEG. NO. 31549

Peace
Signed l.l. Walter L. Dean; 6′ 3″ x 9′
Purchased 1928
311 Cannon House Office Building

194

VICE PRESIDENTS

THIRTY-SEVEN BUSTS

Thirty-seven marble busts of Vice Presidents were acquired under authority of Senate resolutions of January 27, 1885, May 13, 1886, January 6, 1898 and March 28, 1947.

This collection includes all Vice Presidents from the first Vice President, John Adams, through Lyndon B. Johnson. Twenty of these busts are located in niches in the gallery walls of the Senate Chamber, 12 in the second floor corridors of the Senate wing adjacent to the Chamber, 1 in the Vice President's formal office, S–214, and 2 in the Senate Reception Room, S–213.

The busts of Richard M. Nixon and Lyndon B. Johnson have been completed. Because they have not been placed, photographs are not available.

The busts of Hubert H. Humphrey, Spiro T. Agnew, Gerald R. Ford and Nelson A. Rockefeller have not been executed.

Vice President	State	Period of service	Sculptor	Date of purchase
John Adams	Massachusetts	Apr. 30, 1789–Mar. 3, 1797	Daniel Chester French	1890
Thomas Jefferson	Virginia	Mar. 4, 1797–Mar. 3, 1801	Sir Moses Ezekiel	1889
Aaron Burr	New York	Mar. 4, 1801–Mar. 3, 1805	Jacques Jovenal	1893
George Clinton	New York	Mar. 4, 1805–Apr. 20, 1812	Vittorio A. Ciani	1894
Elbridge Gerry	Massachusetts	Mar. 4, 1813–Nov. 23, 1814	Herbert Adams	1892
Daniel D. Tompkins	New York	Mar. 4, 1817–Mar. 3, 1825	Charles H. Niehaus	1891
John C. Calhoun	South Carolina	Mar. 4, 1825–Dec. 28, 1832	Theodore A. Mills	1896
Martin Van Buren	New York	Mar. 4, 1833–Mar. 3, 1837	U. S. J. Dunbar	1894
Richard M. Johnson	Kentucky	Mar. 4, 1837–Mar. 3, 1841	James P. Voorhees	1895
John Tyler	Virginia	Mar. 4, 1841–Apr. 4, 1841	William C. McCauslen	1898
George M. Dallas	Pennsylvania	Mar. 4, 1845–Mar. 3, 1849	Henry J. Ellicott	1893
Millard Fillmore	New York	Mar. 5, 1849–July 9, 1850	Robert Cushing	1895
William R. King	Alabama	Mar. 4, 1853–Apr. 18, 1853	William C. McCauslen	1896
John C. Breckinridge	Kentucky	Mar. 4, 1857–Mar. 3, 1861	James P. Voorhees	1896
Hannibal Hamlin	Maine	Mar. 4, 1861–Mar. 3, 1865	Franklin Simmons	1889
Andrew Johnson	Tennessee	Mar. 4, 1865–Apr. 15, 1865	William C. McCauslen	1900
Schuyler Colfax	Indiana	Mar. 4, 1869–Mar. 3, 1873	Frances M. Goodwin	1897
Henry Wilson	Massachusetts	Mar. 4, 1873–Nov. 22, 1875	Daniel Chester French	1885–86
William A. Wheeler	New York	Mar. 5, 1877–Mar. 3, 1881	Edward C. Potter	1892
Chester A. Arthur	New York	Mar. 4, 1881–Sept. 19, 1881	Augustus Saint-Gaudens	1892
Thomas A. Hendricks	Indiana	Mar. 4, 1885–Nov. 25, 1885	U. S. J. Dunbar	1890
Levi P. Morton	New York	Mar. 4, 1889–Mar. 3, 1893	F. Edwin Elwell	1891
Adlai E. Stevenson	Illinois	Mar. 4, 1893–Mar. 3, 1897	Franklin Simmons	1894
Garret A. Hobart	New Jersey	Mar. 4, 1897–Nov. 21, 1899	F. Edwin Elwell	1901
Theodore Roosevelt	New York	Mar. 4, 1901–Sept. 14, 1901	James Earle Fraser	1910
Charles W. Fairbanks	Indiana	Mar. 4, 1905–Mar. 3, 1909	Franklin Simmons	1909
James S. Sherman	New York	Mar. 4, 1909–Oct. 30, 1912	Bessie Potter Vonnoh	1912
Thomas R. Marshall	Indiana	Mar. 4, 1913–Mar. 3, 1921	Moses A. Wainer Dykaar	1920
Calvin Coolidge	Massachusetts	Mar. 4, 1921–Aug. 2, 1923	Moses A. Wainer Dykaar	1929
Charles G. Dawes	Illinois	Mar. 4, 1925–Mar. 3, 1929	Jo Davidson	1935
Charles Curtis	Kansas	Mar. 4, 1929–Mar. 3, 1933	Moses A. Wainer Dykaar	1935
John Nance Garner	Texas	Mar. 4, 1933–Jan. 20, 1941	James Earle Fraser	1943
Henry A. Wallace	Iowa	Jan. 20, 1941–Jan. 20, 1945	Jo Davidson	1948
Harry S. Truman	Missouri	Jan. 20, 1945–Apr. 12, 1945	Charles Keck	1947
Alben W. Barkley	Kentucky	Jan. 20, 1949–Jan. 20, 1953	Kalervo Kallio	1958
Richard M. Nixon	California	Jan. 20, 1953–Jan. 20, 1961	Gualberto Rocchi	1965
Lyndon B. Johnson	Texas	Jan. 20, 1961–Nov. 22, 1963	Jimilu Mason	1966
Hubert H. Humphrey	Minnesota	Jan. 20, 1965–Jan. 20, 1969		
Spiro T. Agnew	Maryland	Jan. 20, 1969–Oct. 10, 1973		
Gerald R. Ford	Michigan	Dec. 6, 1973–Aug. 9, 1974		
Nelson A. Rockefeller	New York	Dec. 19, 1974–Jan. 20, 1977		

NEG. NO. 25720

JOHN ADAMS, Vice President
Daniel Chester French, 1890, 31″
Senate Chamber gallery

NEG. NO. 25721

CHESTER A. ARTHUR, Vice President
Augustus Saint-Gaudens, 1892, 30″
Senate Chamber gallery

NEG. NO. 25741

ALBEN W. BARKLEY, Vice President
Signed r. side Kalervo Kallio; 1958, 28″
Senate wing, second floor, main corridor

NEG. NO. 36378

JOHN C. BRECKINRIDGE, Vice President
Signed l. side James Paxton Voorhees, Sc.
    A.D. 1896; 30¼″
Senate Chamber gallery

NEG. NO. 25723

AARON BURR, Vice President
Jacques Jouvenal, 1894, 30¾″
Signed r. side Jouvenal
Senate Chamber gallery

NEG. NO. 25724

JOHN C. CALHOUN, Vice President
Theodore A. Mills, 1896, 30″
Signed l. on back Theo. A. Mills
Senate Chamber gallery

NEG. NO. 25725

GEORGE CLINTON, Vice President
Vittorio A. Ciani, 1894, 29¼″
Signed l. side Victor A. Ciani, Sculptor N.Y.
Senate Chamber gallery

NEG. NO. 25726

SCHUYLER COLFAX, Vice President
Signed front r. side Frances M. Goodwin,
    1897; 30¼″
Senate Chamber gallery

201

NEG. NO. 25742

CALVIN COOLIDGE, Vice President
Moses A. Wainer Dykaar, 28″
Signed r. side Moses W. Dykaar, 1927
Senate wing, second floor, east corridor

NEG. NO. 25743

CHARLES CURTIS, Vice President
Moses A. Wainer Dykaar, 24″
Signed r. side Moses Dykaar, 1929
Senate wing, second floor, east corridor

NEG. NO. 25727

GEORGE M. DALLAS, Vice President
Henry J. Ellicott, 1894, 30½″
Senate Chamber gallery

NEG. NO. 25744

CHARLES G. DAWES, Vice President
Jo Davidson, 1931, 25″
Senate wing, second floor, east corridor

CHARLES W. FAIRBANKS, Vice President
Signed on back Franklin Simmons, 1905; 36″
Senate wing, second floor, main corridor

MILLARD FILLMORE, Vice President
Robert Cushing, 1895, 30¼″
Senate Chamber gallery

JOHN N. GARNER, Vice President
James Earle Fraser, 1943, 35″
Signed l. side J. E. Fraser
S–213, Senate Reception Room

ELBRIDGE GERRY, Vice President
Signed on back Herbert Adams MDCCCXCII
    [1892]; 31¾″
Senate Chamber gallery

NEG. NO. 25730

HANNIBAL HAMLIN, Vice President
Franklin Simmons, 1890, 29½"
Senate Chamber gallery

NEG. NO. 25731

THOMAS A. HENDRICKS, Vice President
U.S.J. Dunbar, 1890, 29¼"
Senate Chamber gallery

NEG. NO. 25747

GARRET A. HOBART, Vice President
F. Edwin Elwell, 39"
Signed l. front F. E. Elwell, Sc. 1901
Senate wing, second floor, main corridor

NEG. NO. 25732

THOMAS JEFFERSON, Vice President
Sir Moses Ezekiel, 1889, 29"
Senate Chamber gallery

204

ANDREW JOHNSON, Vice President
William C. McCauslen, 1900, 32″
Senate Chamber gallery

RICHARD M. JOHNSON, Vice President
James P. Voorhees, 31½″
Signed r. side J. P. Voorhees '95
Senate Chamber gallery

WILLIAM R. KING, Vice President
William C. McCauslen, 33″
Signed r. side W. C. M'Causlen '96
Senate Chamber gallery

THOMAS R. MARSHALL, Vice President
Moses A. Wainer Dykaar, 34″
Signed r. side M. A. Dykaar, Capitol 1920
Senate wing, second floor, east corridor

NEG. NO. 25750

Levi P. Morton, Vice President
Signed on plinth F. Edwin Elwell, Sc.; 1891,
34″
Senate wing, second floor, main corridor

NEG. NO. 25751

Theodore Roosevelt, Vice President
James Earle Fraser, 1910, 36″
Signed r. side Fraser
Senate wing, second floor, main corridor

NEG. NO. 25752

James S. Sherman, Vice President
Bessie Potter Vonnoh, 1911, 34″
Senate wing, second floor, main corridor

NEG. NO. 25753

Adlai E. Stevenson, Vice President
Signed on back Franklin Simmons, 1894; 36″
Senate wing, second floor, main corridor

NEG. NO. 25736

DANIEL TOMPKINS, Vice President
Charles H. Niehaus, 1891, 31¼″
Senate Chamber gallery

NEG. NO. 25754

HARRY S. TRUMAN, Vice President
Signed on back Charles Keck, sculptor 19–61;
    28″
Senate wing, second floor, east corridor

NEG. NO. 25737

JOHN TYLER, Vice President
William C. McCauslen, 30¼″
Signed r. side W. C. M'Causlen '98
Senate Chamber gallery

NEG. NO. 25738

MARTIN VAN BUREN, Vice President
Signed on plinth U.S.J. Dunbar, Sc. 1894; 31″
Senate Chamber gallery

207

NEG. NO. 25755

HENRY A. WALLACE, Vice President
Signed r. side Jo Davidson, N.Y., 1947; 23″
S–213, Senate Reception Room

NEG. NO. 25739

WILLIAM A. WHEELER, Vice President
Edward C. Potter, 1892, 30¾″
Senate Chamber gallery

NEG. NO. 25812

HENRY WILSON, Vice President
Daniel Chester French, 1886, 32″
S–214, Vice President's formal office

208

CHIEF JUSTICES

TEN BUSTS

Ten marble busts of Chief Justices of the United States were acquired under appropriation and other authority. Five are located in S–141, which was the Supreme Court Chamber from 1809 to 1860. Five busts were transferred to the U.S. Supreme Court Building in 1973.

Chief Justice	State appointed from	Service	Sculptor	Date of purchase
John Jay	New York	1789–95	John Frazee	1831
John Rutledge	South Carolina	1795	Alexander Galt	1858
Oliver Ellsworth	Connecticut	1796–1800	Hezekiah Augur	1837
John Marshall	Virginia	1801–35	Hiram Powers	1836
Roger B. Taney	Maryland	1836–64	Augustus Saint-Gaudens	1877
Salmon P. Chase [1]	Ohio	1864–73	Thomas D. Jones	1875
Morrison R. Waite [1]	Ohio	1874–88	Augustus Saint-Gaudens	1875
Melville W. Fuller [1]	Illinois	1888–1910	William Ordway Partridge	1891
Edward D. White [1]	Louisiana	1910–21	Bryant Baker	1911
William Howard Taft [1]	Connecticut	1921–30	Bryant Baker	1934

[1] Transferred to the U.S. Supreme Court Building, 1973.

NEG. NO. 34051

SALMON P. CHASE, Chief Justice
Thomas D. Jones, 34''
U.S. Supreme Court Building

NEG. NO. 34048

OLIVER ELLSWORTH, Chief Justice
Hezekiah Augur, 33''
S–141, Old Supreme Court Chamber

NEG. NO. 34053

MELVILLE W. FULLER, Chief Justice
William Ordway Partridge, 27″
Signed r. side Ordway Partridge, 1914
U.S. Supreme Court Building

NEG. NO. 34046

JOHN JAY, Chief Justice
John Frazee, 1831, 30″
Signed front of pedestal J. Frazee, fecit
S–141, Old Supreme Court Chamber

NEG. NO. 34049

JOHN MARSHALL, Chief Justice
Hiram Powers, 33″
S–141, Old Supreme Court Chamber

NEG. NO. 34047

JOHN RUTLEDGE, Chief Justice
Alexander Galt, 38″
Signed on back A. Galt, 1858
S–141, Old Supreme Court Chamber

NEG. NO. 34055

WILLIAM HOWARD TAFT, Chief Justice
Signed r. side Bryant Baker, Sc. 1932; 29″
U.S. Supreme Court Building

NEG. NO. 34050

ROGER B. TANEY, Chief Justice
Augustus Saint-Gaudens, 29″
S–141, Old Supreme Court Chamber

NEG. NO. 34052

MORRISON R. WAITE, Chief Justice
Augustus Saint-Gaudens, 31″
U.S. Supreme Court Building

NEG. NO. 34054

EDWARD D. WHITE, Chief Justice
Bryant Baker, 28″
Signed r. side P. Bryant Baker, Sculptor, 1923
U.S. Supreme Court Building

211

SENATORS

FOUR BUSTS

NEG. NO. 34636

HENRY CLAY
Albert P. Henry, after Hart, miniature, 11″
Signed on back A. P. Henry
Purchased Joint Committee on Library 1881
HB–28

NEG. NO. 25810

LAFAYETTE S. FOSTER
Charles Calverly, marble, 22″
Gift of Mrs. Foster, 1885; accepted by S. Res.
S–214, Vice President's formal office

NEG. NO. 34637

CORDELL HULL
George Conlon, 29″. Signed r. side Conlon
Gift of the Cumberland, Maryland Evening
  and Sunday Times, 1944
Accepted by S. Con. Res. 56, 78th Congress
S–213, Senate Reception Room

NEG. NO. 34638

CHARLES SUMNER
Martin Milmore, marble, 36″
Gift of Anna Shaw Curtis, 1894
Accepted by Joint Committee on Library
Senate wing, third floor, east

BUSTS OF MEMBERS AND SPEAKERS OF THE HOUSE OF REPRESENTATIVES

TEN BUSTS

SPEAKERS

NEG. NO. 24683

NEG. NO. 24684

JOSEPH G. CANNON
Signed r. side Albert Jaegers, Sc., 1913; 24″
Gift of friends, 1913
Accepted by H. Res. 873, 62nd Congress
Cannon House Office Building rotunda

JAMES B. (CHAMP) CLARK
Moses A. Wainer Dykaar, marble, 26″
Signed r. side M. Dykaar, Capital, 1918
Placed 1925 by H. Res. 568, 67th Congress
Cannon House Office Building rotunda

NEG. NO. 24686

NEG. NO. 24689

NICHOLAS LONGWORTH
Moses A. Wainer Dykaar, marble, 24″
Signed r. side Moses Dykaar, 1930
Placed 1932 by H. Res. 44, 72nd Congress
Cannon House Office Building rotunda

JOSEPH W. MARTIN, JR.
Suzanne Silvercruys, marble, 23″
Signed r. side Suzanne Silver, 1962
Gift of Nat'l. Federation of GOP Women, 1962
Accepted by H. Res. 393, 87th Congress
Cannon House Office Building rotunda

NEG. NO. 27755

SAM RAYBURN
Signed l.r. Paul Manship, sculp 1964; marble,
  5′9¾′′ x 2′9′′
Purchased 1964
Rayburn House Office Building, first floor

NEG. NO. 24690

THOMAS BRACKETT REED
Gutzon and Lincoln Borglum, marble, 26′′
Signed r. side Gutzon Borglum, Sc.
Placed 1943 by H. Res. 315, 76th Congress
Cannon House Office Building rotunda

MEMBERS

CLAUDE KITCHIN
Signed l. side Edgardo Simone; marble, 23″
Placed 1931 by H. Res. 95, 71st Congress
Cannon House Office Building rotunda

MARTIN B. MADDEN
Signed l. side Albin Polasek, 1929; 21″
Placed 1929 by H. Res. 226, 70th Congress
Cannon House Office Building rotunda

JAMES R. MANN
Signed r. side Herbert Adams, Sc. MCMXXV
  [1925]; marble, 26″
Placed 1925 by H. Res. 568, 67th Congress
Cannon House Office Building rotunda

OSCAR W. UNDERWOOD
Chester Beach, 34″. Signed l. side Beach, 1933
Placed 1933 by H. Res. 55, 72nd Congress
Cannon House Office Building rotunda

PROMINENT INDIVIDUALS

ELEVEN BUSTS

AYSH-KE-BAH-KE-KO-ZHAY, Chippewa Chief
Signed front By Francis Vincenti; marble, 24″
By employment of artist at the Capitol, 1858
Senate wing, third floor, east corridor

BEESHEKEE (Buffalo), Chippewa warrior
Joseph Lassalle after Vincenti, bronze, 25″
By employment of artist at Capitol, 1858
House wing, west stairway, first floor

BEESHEKEE (Buffalo)
Francis Vincenti, marble, 33″
By employment of artist at Capitol, 1854
Senate wing, third floor, east corridor

CONSTANTINO BRUMIDI
Signed l. side Jimilu Mason © 1967; marble, 28"
Purchased 1966 by the Joint Committee on the
  Library by S. Con. Res. 70, 89th Congress
Brumidi corridor, Senate wing, first floor

Brumidi spent 25 years decorating the capitol.

NEG. NO. 24555

VISCOUNT JAMES BRYCE
Sir William Reid Dick, bronze, 31"
Gift of Sir Charles Cheers Wakefield for the
  Sulgrave Institution of Great Britain, 1922
Accepted by Joint Committee on Library
Senate wing, third floor, east

Ambassador from Great Britain to the U.S. 1907–13.

NEG. NO. 34642

THOMAS CRAWFORD
Tommaso Gagliardi, marble, 34"
Signed on back T. Gagliardi, fecit
Purchased 1871
Senate wing, third floor, east

Crawford, an American sculptor, is represented in
the Capitol by many works of art.

NEG. NO. 23305

GIUSEPPE GARIBALDI
Giuseppe Martegana, marble, 32"
Signed back of bust Martegana
Gift of members of the Italian Society of
  Washington, Citizens of Italian descent, 1888
Accepted by Joint Committee on Library
Lobby opposite entrance to S–141

Italian patriot and soldier, who unified Italy.

217

JOHN PAUL JONES
Antoine Houdon, bronze, 28''
Gift of the Secretary of the Navy, 1948
Accepted by the Joint Committee on the Library
Senate wing, third floor, east

American Naval Officer in Revolutionary War. Bust was cast in 1904 from original 1780 plaster model.

THADDEUS KOSCIUSZKO
H. Dmochowski-Saunders, marble, 35''
Signed r. base H. D. Saunders, 1857
Purchased 1857
Lobby opposite entrance to S–141

Polish-American patriot and statesman, who served in the Revolutionary War.

GENERAL LAFAYETTE
Signed r. side P. J. David d'Angers, 1830;
    marble, 33''. Purchased 1904
Rotunda

French patriot who assisted George Washington during American Revolution. This marble bust replaced the original one destroyed in the Library fire of 1851.

K. K. (CASIMIR) PULASKI
H. Dmochowski-Saunders, marble, 39''
Signed l. base H. Dmochowski, 1857, PHI
Purchased 1882
Lobby opposite entrance to S–141

Polish-American Revolutionary War patriot. Earned the right of American citizenship by giving his life at the siege of Savannah in 1779.

218

NATIONAL STATUARY HALL

The concept of a National Statuary Hall began in the middle of the nineteenth century. The completion of the present House wing in 1857 allowed the House of Representatives to move into its new and larger chamber. The old, vacant, semicircular, marble columned chamber became a cluttered thorough fare between the Rotunda and the House wing.

Suggestions for the use of the old chamber were made as early as 1853 by Gouverneur Kemble, a former member of the House, who pressed for its use as a gallery for historical paintings. The space between the columns seemed too limited for such a purpose, but was considered more suited for the display of busts and statuary.

On April 19, 1864, the Honorable Justin S. Morrill in the House of Representatives proposed: "To what end more useful or grand, and at the same time simple and inexpensive, can we devote it [the Chamber] than to ordain that it shall be set apart for the reception of such statuary as each State shall elect to be deserving of in this lasting commemoration?"

This proposal was enacted into the law creating the National Statuary Hall, July 2, 1864 (sec. 1814 of the Revised Statutes), the essential part of which provides:

And the President is hereby authorized to invite each and all the States to provide and furnish statues, in marble or bronze, not exceeding two in number for each State, of deceased persons who have been citizens thereof, and illustrious for their historic renown or for distinguished civic or military services such as each State may deem to be worthy of this national commemoration; and when so furnished the same shall be placed in the Old Hall of the House of Representatives, in the Capitol of the United States, which is set apart, or so much thereof as may be necessary, as a national statuary hall for the purpose herein indicated.

By 1933, 65 statues were crowded into Statuary Hall. In some places they were lined three deep which was esthetically displeasing. More important, however, the structure of the chamber would not accommodate the excessive weight and there were statues yet to come.

On February 24, 1933, Congress passed House Concurrent Resolution No. 47 to provide for the relocation of statues and to govern the future reception and location of statues.

Resolved by the House of Representatives (the Senate concurring), That the Architect of the Capitol, upon the approva of the Joint Committee on the Library, with the advice of the Commission of Fine Arts, is hereby authorized and directed to relocate within the Capitol any of the statues already received and placed in Statuary Hall, and to provide for the reception and location of the statues received hereafter from the States.

Under authority of this resolution, it was decided that only one statue from each State should be placed in Statuary Hall. The other statues were located prominently in designated areas and corridors of the Capitol.

A second rearrangement of the statues was made in 1976 by authorization of the Joint Committee on the Library to reduce overcrowding and to improve the aesthetic quality and orderliness of the physical arrangement of the National Statuary Hall Collection. Statues were placed in the East Central Hall of the east front extension on the first floor of the Capitol. Other statues were relocated within the corridors, Hall of Columns and Statuary Hall.

Ninety-two statues, 45 marble and 47 bronze, have been contributed by 50 States. Two statues have been contributed by 41 States. One statue has been received from each of the following 8 States: Colorado, Montana, Nevada, New Mexico, North Dakota, Utah, Washington and Wyoming.

STATUES BY STATES

State	Statue	Sculptor
Alabama	Jabez Lamar Monroe Curry	Dante Sodini
	General Joseph Wheeler	Berthold Nebel
Alaska	E. L. "Bob" Bartlett	Felix W. de Weldon
	Ernest Gruening *	George Anthonisen
Arizona	John Campbell Greenway	Gutzon Borglum
	Eusebio F. Kino	Suzanne Silvercruys
Arkansas	Uriah M. Rose	Frederic W. Ruckstuhl
	James Paul Clarke	Pompeo Coppini
California	Thomas Starr King	Haig Patigian
	Junipero Serra	Ettore Cadorin
Colorado	Dr. Florence Rena Sabin	Joy Buba
Connecticut	Roger Sherman	Chauncey B. Ives
	Jonathan Trumbull	Chauncey B. Ives
Delaware	Caesar Rodney	Bryant Baker
	John Middleton Clayton	Bryant Baker
Florida	Dr. John Gorrie	Charles Adrian Pillars
	Gen. Edmund Kirby Smith	Charles Adrian Pillars
Georgia	Dr. Crawford W. Long	J. Massey Rhind
	Alexander H. Stephens	Gutzon Borglum
Hawaii	King Kamehameha I	Thomas R. Gould
	Father Damien	Marisol Escobar
Idaho	George L. Shoup	Frederick Ernst Triebel
	William Edgar Borah	Bryant Baker
Illinois	General James Shields	Leonard Wells Volk
	Frances E. Willard	Helen Farnsworth Mears
Indiana	Oliver Hazard Perry (Throck) Morton	Charles H. Niehaus
	General Lew Wallace	Andrew O'Connor
Iowa	James Harlan	Nellie V. Walker
	Samuel Jordan Kirkwood	Vinnie Ream
Kansas	John James Ingalls	Charles H. Niehaus
	George Washington Glick	Charles H. Niehaus
Kentucky	Henry Clay	Charles H. Niehaus
	Dr. Ephraim McDowell	Charles H. Niehaus
Louisiana	Huey Pierce Long	Charles Keck
	Edward Douglass White	Arthur C. Morgan
Maine	William King	Franklin Simmons
	Hannibal Hamlin	Charles E. Tefft
Maryland	Charles Carroll of Carrollton	Richard E. Brooks
	John Hanson	Richard E. Brooks
Massachusetts	Samuel Adams	Anne Whitney
	John Winthrop	Richard S. Greenough
Michigan	Lewis Cass	Daniel Chester French
	Zachariah Chandler	Charles H. Niehaus
Minnesota	Henry Mower Rice	Frederick Ernst Triebel
	Maria L. Sanford	Evelyn Raymond
Mississippi	Jefferson Davis	Augustus Lukeman
	James Zachariah George	Augustus Lukeman
Missouri	Francis P. Blair, Jr.	Alexander Doyle
	Thomas Hart Benton	Alexander Doyle

* Unveiled Oct. 1977.

State	Statue	Sculptor
Montana	Charles Marion Russell	John B. Weaver
Nebraska	William Jennings Bryan	Rudulph Evans
	J. Sterling Morton	Rudulph Evans
Nevada	Patrick Anthony McCarran	Yolande Jacobson
New Hampshire	John Stark	Carl Conrads
	Daniel Webster	Carl Conrads
New Jersey	Richard Stockton	Henry K. Brown and H. K. Bush-Brown
	Philip Kearny	Henry Kirke Brown
New Mexico	Dennis Chavez	Felix W. de Weldon
New York	Robert Livingston	Erastus Dow Palmer
	George Clinton	Henry Kirke Brown
North Carolina	Zebulon Baird Vance	Gutzon Borglum
	Charles Brantley Aycock	Charles Keck
North Dakota	John Burke	Avard Fairbanks
Ohio	James Garfield	Charles H. Niehaus
	William Allen	Charles H. Niehaus
Oklahoma	Sequoyah (Sequoya)	Vinnie Ream and G. Julian Zolnay
	Will Rogers	Jo Davidson
Oregon	Reverend Jason Lee	Gifford Proctor
	John McLoughlin	Gifford Proctor
Pennsylvania	John Peter Gabriel Muhlenberg	Blanche Nevin
	Robert Fulton	Howard Roberts
Rhode Island	Nathanael Greene	Henry Kirke Brown
	Roger Williams	Franklin Simmons
South Carolina	John C. Calhoun	Frederic W. Ruckstull
	Wade Hampton	Frederic W. Ruckstull
South Dakota	William H. H. Beadle	H. Daniel Webster
	Joseph Ward	Bruno Beghe
Tennessee	Andrew Jackson	Belle K. Scholz and L. F. Scholz
	John Sevier	Belle K. Scholz and L. F. Scholz
Texas	Stephen F. Austin	Elisabet Ney
	Samuel Houston	Elisabet Ney
Utah	Brigham Young	Mahonri Young
Vermont	Ethan Allen	Larkin G. Mead
	Jacob Collamer	Preston Powers
Virginia	Robert E. Lee	Edward V. Valentine
	George Washington	Antoine Houdon
Washington	Marcus Whitman	Avard Fairbanks
West Virginia	John E. Kenna	Alexander Doyle
	Francis H. Pierpont	Franklin Simmons
Wisconsin	Pere Jacques Marquette	Gaetano Trentanove
	Robert Marion La Follette, Sr.	Jo Davidson
Wyoming	Esther Hobart Morris	Avard Fairbanks

ALPHABETICAL LIST OF THE 92 STATUES IN THE NATIONAL STATUARY HALL COLLECTION

Statue	State	Sculptor	Medium	Unveiling or congressional proceedings	Location
Adams, Samuel	Massachusetts	Anne Whitney	Marble	Congressional Proceedings 1876	E. Central Hall
Allen, Ethan	Vermont	Larkin G. Mead	Marble	Congressional Proceedings 1876	Statuary Hall
Allen, William	Ohio	Charles H. Niehaus	Marble	Placed 1887	Statuary Hall
Austin, Stephen F.	Texas	Elisabet Ney	Marble	Congressional Proceedings 1905	Small House rotunda
Aycock, Charles Brantley	North Carolina	Charles Keck	Bronze	Unveiled 1932	E. Central Hall
Bartlett, E. L. "Bob"	Alaska	Felix W. de Weldon	Bronze	Unveiled 1971	House connecting corridor
Beadle, William H. H.	South Dakota	H. Daniel Webster	Bronze	Unveiled 1938	Statuary Hall
Benton, Thomas H.	Missouri	Alexander Doyle	Marble	Congressional Proceedings 1899	Statuary Hall
Blair, Francis P., Jr.	Missouri	Alexander Doyle	Marble	Congressional Proceedings 1899	Hall of Columns
Borah, William E.	Idaho	Bryant Baker	Bronze	Unveiled 1947	Senate connecting corridor
Bryan, William Jennings	Nebraska	Rudulph Evans	Bronze	Unveiled 1937	Statuary Hall
Burke, John	North Dakota	Avard Fairbanks	Bronze	Unveiled 1963	Statuary Hall
Calhoun, John C.	South Carolina	Frederic W. Ruckstull	Marble	Unveiled 1910	E. Central Hall
Carroll, Charles, of Carrollton	Maryland	Richard E. Brooks	Bronze	Congressional Proceedings 1903	E. Central Hall
Cass, Lewis	Michigan	Daniel Chester French	Marble	Congressional Proceedings 1889	Statuary Hall
Chandler, Zachariah	Michigan	Charles H. Niehaus	Marble	Unveiled 1913	Hall of Columns
Chavez, Dennis	New Mexico	Felix W. de Weldon	Bronze	Unveiled 1966	Vestibule north of Rotunda
Clarke, James P.	Arkansas	Pompeo Coppini	Marble	Placed 1921	Hall of Columns
Clay, Henry	Kentucky	Charles H. Niehaus	Bronze	Unveiled 1929	Statuary Hall
Clayton, John M.	Delaware	Bryant Baker	Marble	Unveiled 1934	Senate connecting corridor
Clinton, George	New York	Henry Kirke Brown	Bronze	Placed 1873	Small House rotunda
Collamer, Jacob	Vermont	Preston Powers	Marble	Congressional Proceedings 1881	Hall of Columns
Curry, Jabez Lamar Monroe	Alabama	Dante Sodini	Marble	Congressional Proceedings 1908	Hall of Columns
Damien, Father	Hawaii	Marisol Escobar	Bronze	Unveiled 1969	Hall of Columns
Davis, Jefferson	Mississippi	Augustus Lukeman	Bronze	Unveiled 1931	Statuary Hall
Fulton, Robert	Pennsylvania	Howard Roberts	Marble	Congressional Proceedings 1889	Statuary Hall
Garfield, James A.	Ohio	Charles H. Niehaus	Marble	Congressional Proceedings 1886	Rotunda
George, James Z.	Mississippi	Augustus Lukeman	Bronze	Unveiled 1931	Hall of Columns
Glick, George W.	Kansas	Charles H. Niehaus	Marble	Congressional Proceedings 1914	Hall of Columns
Gorrie, John	Florida	C. A. Pillars	Marble	Unveiled 1914	Statuary Hall
Greene, Nathanael	Rhode Island	Henry Kirke Brown	Marble	Congressional Proceedings 1870	E. Central Hall
Greenway, John C.	Arizona	Gutzon Borglum	Bronze	Unveiled 1930	Statuary Hall
Gruening, Ernest	Alaska	George Anthonisen	Bronze	Unveiled 1977	Hall of Columns
Hamlin, Hannibal	Maine	Charles E. Tefft	Bronze	Unveiled 1935	Statuary Hall

Statue	State	Sculptor	Medium	Unveiling or congressional proceedings	Location
Hampton, Wade	South Carolina	Frederic W. Ruckstull	Marble	Unveiled 1929	House connecting corridor
Hanson, John	Maryland	Richard E. Brooks	Bronze	Congressional Proceedings (1903)	Senate connecting corridor
Harlan, James	Iowa	Nellie V. Walker	Bronze	Installed 1910	Hall of Columns
Houston, Samuel	Texas	Elisabet Ney	Marble	Congressional Proceedings 1905	Statuary Hall
Ingalls, John J.	Kansas	Charles H. Niehaus	Marble	Congressional Proceedings 1905	Statuary Hall
Jackson, Andrew	Tennessee	Belle Kinney Scholz and Leopold F. Scholz	Bronze	Unveiled 1928	Rotunda
Kamehameha I	Hawaii	Thomas R. Gould	Bronze	Unveiled 1969	Statuary Hall
Kearny, Philip	New Jersey	Henry Kirke Brown	Bronze	Congressional Proceedings 1888	Hall of Columns
Kenna, John E.	West Virginia	Alexander Doyle	Marble	Placed 1901	Hall of Columns
King, Thomas Starr	California	Haig Patigian	Bronze	Unveiled 1931	Hall of Columns
King, William	Maine	Franklin Simmons	Marble	Congressional Proceedings 1878	House connecting corridor
Kino, Eusebio F.	Arizona	Suzanne Silvercruys	Bronze	Unveiled 1965	Hall of Columns
Kirkwood, Samuel J.	Iowa	Vinnie Ream	Bronze	Placed 1913	Statuary Hall
La Follette, Robert M.,	Wisconsin	Jo Davidson	Marble	Unveiled 1929	Statuary Hall
Lee, Rev. Jason	Oregon	Gifford Proctor [1]	Bronze	Unveiled 1953	Statuary Hall
Lee, Robert E.	Virginia	Edward V. Valentine	Bronze	Unveiled 1934	Statuary Hall
Livingston, Robert R.	New York	Erastus Dow Palmer	Bronze	Placed 1875	E. Central Hall
Long, Dr. Crawford W.	Georgia	J. Massey Rhind	Marble	Unveiled 1926	E. Central Hall
Long, Huey P.	Louisiana	Charles Keck	Bronze	Unveiled 1941	Statuary Hall
Marquette, Pere Jacques	Wisconsin	Gaetano Trentanove	Marble	Congressional Proceedings 1896	House connecting corridor
McCarran, Patrick A.	Nevada	Yolande Jacobson	Bronze	Unveiled 1960	Statuary Hall vestibule north
McDowell, Dr. Ephraim	Kentucky	Charles H. Niehaus	Bronze	Unveiled 1929	Senate connecting corridor
McLoughlin, Dr. John	Oregon	Gifford Proctor [1]	Bronze	Unveiled 1953	House connecting corridor
Morris, Esther H.	Wyoming	Avard Fairbanks	Bronze	Unveiled 1960	Statuary Hall vestibule north
Morton J. Sterling	Nebraska	Rudulph Evans	Bronze	Unveiled 1937	Hall of Columns
Morton, Oliver P.	Indiana	Charles H. Niehaus	Marble	Congressional Proceedings 1900	Hall of Columns
Muhlenberg, John P. G.	Pennsylvania	Blanche Nevin	Marble	Congressional Proceedings 1889	Small House rotunda
Pierpont, Francis H.	West Virginia	Franklin Simmons	Marble	Unveiled 1910	Statuary Hall
Rice, Henry Mower	Minnesota	Frederick E. Triebel	Marble	Unveiled 1916	Statuary Hall
Rodney, Caesar	Delaware	Bryant Baker	Marble	Unveiled 1934	E. Central Hall
Rogers, Will	Oklahoma	Jo Davidson	Bronze	Unveiled 1939	House connecting corridor

[1] Joint commission for the Oregon statues was given to A. Phimister Proctor and his son, Gifford. Phimister died before the models were completed and the statues were executed by Gifford (G. MacG.).

Statue	State	Sculptor	Medium	Unveiling or congressional proceedings	Location
Rose, Uriah M.	Arkansas	Frederic W. Ruckstuhl	Marble	Placed 1917	Statuary Hall
Russell, Charles M.	Montana	John B. Weaver	Bronze	Unveiled 1959	Statuary Hall
Sabin, Dr. Florence R.	Colorado	Joy Buba	Bronze	Unveiled 1959	Statuary Hall
Sanford, Maria L.	Minnesota	Evelyn Raymond	Bronze	Unveiled 1958	Senate connecting corridor
Sequoyah (Sequoya)	Oklahoma	Vinnie Ream (completed by G. Julian Zolnay)	Bronze	Unveiled 1917	Statuary Hall
Serra, Junipero	California	Ettore Cadorin	Bronze	Unveiled 1931	Statuary Hall
Sevier, John	Tennessee	Belle Kinney Scholz and Leopold F. Scholz	Bronze	Unveiled 1931	Statuary Hall
Sherman, Roger	Connecticut	Chauncey B. Ives	Marble	Congressional Proceedings 1872	E. Central Hall
Shields, Gen. James	Illinois	Leonard W. Volk	Bronze	Unveiled 1893	Hall of Columns
Shoup, George L.	Idaho	Frederick E. Triebel	Marble	Congressional Proceedings 1910	Statuary Hall
Smith, Gen. E. Kirby	Florida	C. Adrian Pillars	Bronze	Congressional Proceedings 1922	Hall of Columns
Stark, John	New Hampshire	Carl Conrads	Marble	Congressional Proceedings 1894	Vestibule north of Rotunda
Stephens, Alexander H.	Georgia	Gutzon Borglum	Marble	Unveiled 1927	Statuary Hall
Stockton, Richard	New Jersey	Henry Kirke Brown (completed by H. K. Bush-Brown)	Marble	Congressional Proceedings 1888	E. Central Hall
Trumbull, Jonathan	Connecticut	Chauncey B. Ives	Marble	Congressional Proceedings 1872	House connecting corridor
Vance, Zebulon Baird	North Carolina	Gutzon Borglum	Bronze	Unveiled 1916	Statuary Hall
Wallace, General Lew	Indiana	Andrew O'Connor	Marble	Unveiled 1910	Statuary Hall
Ward, Joseph	South Dakota	Bruno Beghé	Marble	Unveiled 1963	Hall of Columns
Washington, George	Virginia	Antoine Houdon	Bronze	Unveiled 1934	Rotunda
Webster, Daniel	New Hampshire	Carl Conrads (after Thomas Ball)	Marble	Congressional Proceedings 1894	Statuary Hall
Wheeler, General Joseph	Alabama	Berthold Nebel	Bronze	Unveiled 1925	Statuary Hall
White, Edward Douglass	Louisiana	Arthur C. Morgan	Bronze	Unveiled 1955	Senate connecting corridor
Whitman, Marcus	Washington	Avard Fairbanks	Bronze	Unveiled 1953	Statuary Hall
Willard, Frances E.	Illinois	Helen Farnsworth Mears	Marble	Congressional Proceedings 1905	Statuary Hall
Williams, Roger	Rhode Island	Franklin Simmons	Marble	Congressional Proceedings 1872	E. Central Hall
Winthrop, John	Massachusetts	Richard S. Greenough	Marble	Congressional Proceedings 1876	Hall of Columns
Young, Brigham	Utah	Mahonri Young	Marble	Unveiled 1950	Statuary Hall

LOCATIONS OF STATUES

40 STATUES IN STATUARY HALL

State	Statue	Sculptor
Alabama	General Joseph Wheeler	Berthold Nebel
Arizona	John Campbell Greenway	Gutzon Borglum
Arkansas	Uriah M. Rose	Frederic W. Ruckstuhl
California	Junipero Serra	Ettore Cadorin
Colorado	Dr. Florence Rena Sabin	Joy Buba
Florida	John Gorrie	Charles Adrian Pillars
Georgia	Alexander H. Stephens	Gutzon Borglum
Hawaii	King Kamehameha I	Thomas R. Gould
Idaho	George L. Shoup	Frederick Ernst Triebel
Illinois	Frances E. Willard	Helen Farnsworth Mears
Indiana	General Lew Wallace	Andrew O'Connor
Iowa	Samuel J. Kirkwood	Vinnie Ream
Kansas	John J. Ingalls	Charles H. Niehaus
Kentucky	Henry Clay	Charles H. Niehaus
Louisiana	Huey P. Long	Charles Keck
Maine	Hannibal Hamlin	Charles E. Tefft
Michigan	Lewis Cass	Daniel Chester French
Minnesota	Henry M. Rice	Frederick Ernst Triebel
Mississippi	Jefferson Davis	Augustus Lukeman
Missouri	Thomas H. Benton	Alexander Doyle
Montana	Charles Marion Russell	John B. Weaver
Nebraska	William Jennings Bryan	Rudulph Evans
Nevada	Patrick A. McCarran	Yolande Jacobson
New Hampshire	Daniel Webster	Carl Conrads
North Carolina	Zebulon B. Vance	Gutzon Borglum
North Dakota	John Burke	Avard Fairbanks
Ohio	William Allen	Charles H. Niehaus
Oklahoma	Sequoyah (Sequoya)	Vinnie Ream
Oregon	Rev. Jason Lee	Gifford MacG. Proctor
Pennsylvania	Robert Fulton	Howard Roberts
South Dakota	Gen. William Henry H. Beadle	H. Daniel Webster
Tennessee	John Sevier	Belle K. and L. F. Scholz
Texas	Samuel Houston	Elisabet Ney
Utah	Brigham Young	Mahronri Young
Vermont	Ethan Allen	Larkin G. Mead
Virginia	Robert E. Lee	Edward V. Valentine
Washington	Marcus Whitman	Avard Fairbanks
West Virginia	Francis H. Pierpont	Franklin Simmons
Wisconsin	Robert M. La Follette, Sr.	Jo Davidson
Wyoming	Esther H. Morris	Avard Fairbanks

State	Statue	Sculptor

3 STATUES IN THE ROTUNDA

State	Statue	Sculptor
Ohio	James A. Garfield	Charles H. Niehaus
Tennessee	Andrew Jackson	Belle K. Scholz and L. F. Scholz
Virginia	George Washington	Antoine Houdon

3 STATUES IN THE SMALL HOUSE ROTUNDA

State	Statue	Sculptor
New York	George Clinton	Henry Kirke Brown
Pennsylvania	J. P. G. Muhlenberg	Blanche Nevin
Texas	Stephen F. Austin	Elisabet Ney

2 STATUES IN THE VESTIBULE NORTH OF THE ROTUNDA

State	Statue	Sculptor
New Hampshire	John Stark	Carl Conrads
New Mexico	Dennis Chavez	Felix W. de Weldon

6 STATUES IN THE SENATE CONNECTING CORRIDOR

State	Statue	Sculptor
Delaware	John M. Clayton	Bryant Baker
Idaho	William E. Borah	Bryant Baker
Kentucky	Dr. Ephraim McDowell	Charles H. Niehaus
Louisiana	Edward D. White	Arthur C. Morgan
Maryland	John Hanson	Richard E. Brooks
Minnesota	Maria L. Sanford	Evelyn Raymond

7 STATUES IN THE HOUSE CONNECTING CORRIDOR

State	Statue	Sculptor
Alaska	E. L. "Bob" Bartlett	Felix W. de Weldon
Connecticut	Jonathan Trumbull	Chauncey B. Ives
Maine	William King	Franklin Simmons
Oklahoma	Will Rogers	Jo Davidson
Oregon	Dr. John McLoughlin	Gifford MacG. Proctor
South Carolina	Wade Hampton	Frederic W. Ruckstull
Wisconsin	Pere Jacques Marquette	Gaetano Trentanove

10 STATUES IN THE EAST CENTRAL HALL

State	Statue	Sculptor
Connecticut	Roger Sherman	Chauncey B. Ives
Delaware	Caesar Rodney	Bryant Baker
Georgia	Dr. Crawford W. Long	J. Massey Rhind
Massachusetts	Samuel Adams	Anne Whitney
Maryland	Charles Carroll of Carrollton	Richard E. Brooks
New Jersey	Richard Stockton	Henry K. Brown
New York	Robert R. Livingston	Erastus D. Palmer
North Carolina	Charles B. Aycock	Charles Keck
Rhode Island	Nathanael Greene	Henry K. Brown
South Carolina	John C. Calhoun	Frederic W. Ruckstuhl

State	Statue	Sculptor

20 STATUES IN THE HALL OF COLUMNS

State	Statue	Sculptor
Alabama	J. L. M. Curry	Dante Sodini
Alaska	**Ernest Greuning**	George Anthonisen
Arizona	Eusebio F. Kino	Suzanne Silvercruys
Arkansas	James P. Clarke	Pompeo Coppini
California	Thomas Starr King	Haig Patigian
Florida	General Edmund Kirby Smith	Charles Adrian Pillars
Hawaii	Father Damien	Marisol Escobar
Illinois	General James Shields	Leonard W. Volk
Indiana	Oliver P. Morton	Charles H. Niehaus
Iowa	James Harlan	Nellie V. Walker
Kansas	George W. Glick	Charles H. Niehaus
Massachusetts	John Winthrop	Richard S. Greenough
Michigan	Zachariah Chandler	Charles H. Niehaus
Mississippi	James Z. George	Augustus Lukeman
Missouri	Francis P. Blair, Jr.	Alexander Doyle
Nebraska	J. Sterling Morton	Rudulph Evans
New Jersey	General Philip Kearny	Henry Kirke Brown
Rhode Island	**Roger Williams**	**Franklin Simmons**
South Dakota	Joseph Ward	Bruno Beghé
Vermont	Jacob Collamer	Preston Powers
West Virginia	John E. Kenna	Alexander Doyle

SAMUEL ADAMS, 1722–1803, Massachusetts
Signed back of base Anne Whitney; back of
    tree stump A. W. Boston, 1876; marble, 7'8''
East Central Hall

Patriot and called "Father of the American Revolution" and signer of the Declaration of Independence.
Member of General Court of Mass. 1765–74; Continental Congress 1774–82; Mass. Constitutional Convention 1779; president of Mass. State senate 1781;
member of state convention which ratified U.S. Constitution 1788; Lieutenant-Governor of Mass. 1789–94;
Governor 1794–97.

ETHAN ALLEN, 1737–1789, Vermont
Larkin G. Mead, executed about 1874–75,
    marble, 8'8''
Signed back of base L. G. Mead
Statuary Hall

Revolutionary soldier and author. Served in the
French and Indian War; Colonel of the Green Moun-
tain Boys 1770; caused Fort Ticonderoga to surrender
1775; rose to rank of Brigadier General in the Vermont
Militia; prepared Vermont for admission into the
Federal Union.

228

STEPHEN F. AUSTIN, 1793–1836, Texas
Signed r. base Elisabet Ney, fec., Austin, Texas,
  1904; marble, 6′2″
Small House rotunda

Colonizer and patriot. Under a contract with Mexico,
was given judicial and military control of the local
Mexican State of Texas. He assisted in bringing about the
recognition of Texas independence 1836. As Secretary
of the Lone Star Republic of Texas he paved the way for
annexation to the United States, but did not live to see it
accomplished.

WILLIAM ALLEN, 1803–1879, Ohio
Charles H. Niehaus, 1885–87, marble, 7′5″
Signed l. base Niehaus
Statuary Hall

Lawyer, statesman, Governor. Member of the U.S.
House of Representatives 1833–35; member of the U.S.
Senate 1837–49; Governor 1874–76.

NEG. NO. 35021

NEG. NO. 35022

CHARLES BRANTLEY AYCOCK, 1859–1912, North Carolina
Signed l. base Charles Keck, Sc.; executed 1929–32, bronze, 7'3"
East Central Hall

Lawyer, educator and Governor. Superintendent of Public Instruction, Wayne County 1881; U.S. district attorney 1893–97; Governor of North Carolina 1901–05.

EDWARD LEWIS "BOB" BARTLETT, 1904–1968, Alaska
Signed r. base Felix De Weldon, S.C., 1971; bronze, 8'6"
House connecting corridor

Reporter, gold miner, Secretary of Alaska, Delegate to Congress 1945–59; U.S. Senator 1959–68. His instrumentality in gaining Statehood for Alaska has given him the title "Architect of Alaska Statehood."

230

WILLIAM HENRY HARRISON BEADLE, 1838–1915,
South Dakota

Signed front base of column Copyright by the
Sculptor H. Daniel Webster 1911; bronze,
6′4″

Statuary Hall

Educator, conservationist, statesman, soldier, lawyer,
engineer. Instrumental in saving 20 million acres of
school lands in S. Dak., N. Dak., Mont., Wash., Idaho
and Wyoming from speculators. Territorial superintendent of Public Instruction, 1879, and president of
Madison Normal School. Rose from enlisted man to
Brigadier General in the Civil War.

THOMAS HART BENTON, 1782–1858, Missouri
Alexander Doyle, executed 1895–97, marble,
7′7″

Statuary Hall

Author, lawyer, statesman. Member of tne Tenn.
legislature 1809–11; Aide-de-camp to General Jackson
in the War of 1812; editor of the "Missouri Inquirer";
U.S. Senator 1821–51; member of the U.S. House of
Representatives 1853–55, and author of *The Thirty
Years View*, and *Abridgment of the Debates of Congress
from 1789–1850*.

Francis P. Blair, Jr., 1821–1875, Missouri
Alexander Doyle, executed 1895–97, marble,
  7′6″
Hall of Columns

Soldier, lawyer and statesman; served in War with
Mexico. Member of the Missouri general assembly;
served in the U.S. House of Representatives intermittently from 1852 to 1864, and the U.S. Senate 1871–73.

William Edgar Borah, 1865–1940, Idaho
Signed top r. base Bryant Baker, Sculptor, 1946;
  bronze, 7′2″
Senate connecting corridor

Lawyer, legislator, statesman and orator. Renown for
his distinguished service in foreign affairs; U.S. Senator
1907–40. Known as the Lone Lion of Idaho.

232

NEG. NO. 35026

NEG. NO. 35027

WILLIAM JENNINGS BRYAN, 1860–1925, Nebraska
Rudulph Evans, executed 1936–37, bronze,
6'7''
Signed r. base R. Evans
Statuary Hall

Soldier, lawyer, orator and statesman. Member of the
U.S. House of Representatives 1891–95; 3 times an
unsuccessful candidate for President of the United States;
Colonel in the Spanish-American War 1898; founder of
The Commoner newspaper 1901; a zealous worker in
religious and civic interests; Secretary of State under
President Wilson 1913–15.

JOHN BURKE, 1859–1937, North Dakota
Signed r. base Avard Fairbanks, 1962; bronze,
8'6''
Statuary Hall

"North Dakota's Lincoln"; jurist, statesman; State
representative 1890; State senator 1892; Governor 1906;
Treasurer of the U.S. 1913–21 under Woodrow Wilson;
chief justice of the State supreme court.

233

JOHN C. CALHOUN, 1782–1850, South Carolina
Frederic W. Ruckstuhl, marble, 7′7″
Signed r. base F. W. RUCKSTUHL, S.C./1909
East Central Hall

Lawyer, statesman, orator and Vice President of the
United States; leader of a school of earnest men who
believed secession was warranted or at least permissible
under the Constitution of the United States because not
expressly forbidden. State house of representatives
1808–09; U.S. House of Representatives 1811–17;
Secretary of War 1817–25; Vice President 1825–32;
U.S. Senator 1832–43, 1845–50; Secretary of State
1844–45.

CHARLES CARROLL OF CARROLLTON, 1737–1832,
 Maryland
Signed l. base Richard E. Brooks, Sc., Paris
 MCMII [1902]; bronze, 7′6″
East Central Hall

Lawyer, patriot, statesman and signer of the Declaration of Independence. Commissioner to Canada 1776;
delegate to the Continental Congress 1776–78; Member
of Maryland state senate 1777–1800. U.S. Senator 1789–
92; and was the last surviving signer of the Declaration
of Independence.

LEWIS CASS, 1782–1866, Michigan
Daniel Chester French, marble, 7'8''
Signed l. base D. C. French, 1888, Sculptor
Statuary Hall

Soldier, diplomat and statesman. Member of the Ohio
house of representatives; Brigadier General during the
War of 1812; Governor of Territory of Michigan 1813–
1831. Secretary of War under Jackson 1831–36; U.S.
Minister to France 1836–42; U.S. Senator 1845–48,
1849–57; and Secretary of State under Buchanan 1857–
60; an unsuccessful candidate for President. He left
the Cabinet of Buchanan when secession was imminent.

ZACHARIAH CHANDLER, 1813–1879, Michigan
Charles H. Niehaus, executed 1912, marble, 7'7''
Hall of Columns

Opposed secession and slavery above all else; aided in
organizing the Republican Party; U.S. Senator 1857–75;
became the confidant of Lincoln and steadfastly advo-
cated the principles of his party. Secretary of Interior
1875–77 under President Grant.

DENNIS CHAVEZ, 1888–1962, New Mexico
Signed top l. base Felix de Weldon, Sc.; exe-
    cuted 1966, bronze, 7'5"
Vestibule north of Rotunda

Lawyer, U.S. Representative 1931–35; U.S. Senator
1935–62. Served in New Mexico legislature and introduced the first bill to provide free textbooks in the public
schools. Proud of his Spanish ancestry, received the
Order of Aztec Eagle from the Mexican Government;
influenced legislation establishing the Pan-American
highway.

JAMES P. CLARKE, 1854–1916, Arkansas
Signed r. base Pompeo Coppini, Sculptor,
    Chicago; executed 1917–21, marble, 6'10"
Hall of Columns

Lawyer, State attorney general, Governor of Arkansas,
and U.S. Senator from March 4, 1903 until the time of
his death, October 1, 1916; served as President pro
tempore of the Senate 1913–16.

NEG. NO. 35030

NEG. NO. 27493

Henry Clay, 1777–1852, Kentucky
Charles H. Niehaus, bronze, 7'2"
Signed r. base C. H. Niehaus, Sculptor, 1928
Statuary Hall

Lawyer, statesman, parliamentarian, orator. U.S. Senator 1806–07 (in contravention of the 30-year age requirement of the Constitution) and also served intermittently from 1810 until his death in 1852. Member of the Kentucky legislature 1808–09; U.S. House of Representatives intermittently 1811 to 1825. Chosen to the Speakership the day he became a Member, an unprecedented distinction. Peace Commissioner to Great Britain 1814; Secretary of State under John Quincy Adams 1825–29.

John M. Clayton, 1796–1856, Delaware
Signed l. base Bryant Baker, Sc. 1932; marble, 7'6"
Senate connecting corridor

Noted as a jurist, a statesman and a diplomat. State house of representatives, secretary of state and chief justice; Member of the U.S. Senate 1829–36 and 1845–49, when he resigned to accept position of Secretary of State under President Taylor; negotiated the Clayton-Bulwer Treaty; again elected to the U.S. Senate 1853 until his death.

237

NEG. NO. 35031

NEG. NO. 35031

NEG. NO. 28002

GEORGE CLINTON, 1739–1812, New York
Henry Kirke Brown, bronze, 6'8''
Signed front base H. K. Brown, Sculpt. 1873
Small House rotunda

Lawyer, soldier, Governor and Vice President. Fought in the French and Indian War and as a Brigadier General in the Revolutionary War; delegate to the Continental Congress, 1775; first Governor of N.Y. 1777–95, 1801–1804; President of the N.Y. convention ratifying the U.S. Constitution; and Vice President of the U.S. under both Jefferson and Madison.

JACOB COLLAMER, 1792–1865, Vermont
Preston Powers, marble, 6'8''
Signed r. base P. Powers, Sculp. 1879
Hall of Columns

Soldier, orator, jurist, statesman. Served in the War of 1812; Member of the State house of representatives, 1821–22, 1827–28; State's attorney 1822–24; Judge of the Superior Court, 1833–42; 1850–54; elected to U.S. House of Representatives 1843–49; Postmaster General under Taylor 1849–50; U.S. Senator 1855–65.

238

NEG. NO. 35032

NEG. NO. 35034

JABEZ, LAMAR MONROE CURRY, 1825–1903,
  Alabama
Signed r. base Dante Sodini, Florence, Italy;
  1904–06, marble, 7'4''
Hall of Columns

  Soldier, statesman, educator and orator; served in the
War with Mexico and the Civil War; Member of the
U.S. House of Representatives 1857–61; resigned to become a member of the Confederate Congress 1861–64;
professor and college president; Minister to Spain.

FATHER DAMIEN SS.CC., 1840–1889, Hawaii
Marisol Escobar, bronze, 7'7''
Signed r. side of cane Marisol 1968
Hall of Columns

  Born Joseph de Veuster in Tremeloo, Belgium. Became a member of the Congregation of the Sacred
Hearts, given the name Damien. Missionary to Hawaii
and ordained a Priest shortly after his arrival in 1864.
Went to the leper colony on the island of Molokai in
1873 where he lived, labored and died of leprosy after
16 years devoted to improving the conditions in the
colony. Often referred to as the Martyr of Molokai.

239

JEFFERSON DAVIS, 1808–1889, Mississippi
Signed r. base Augustus Lukeman, Sc. 1928;
  bronze, 7'7''
Statuary Hall

Soldier, statesman, President of the Confederacy. A graduate of West Point; fought in the Black Hawk War, 1830–31; the War with Mexico. As Secretary of War under President Pierce 1853–57 he had jurisdiction over the erection of the new House and Senate wings and dome of the U.S. Capitol. U.S. House of Representatives 1845–46; U.S. Senator 1847–51, 1857–61. Elected President of the Southern Confederacy 1862.

ROBERT FULTON, 1765–1815, Pennsylvania
Signed front base Howard Roberts, Philada.,
  1883; marble, 5'4''
Statuary Hall

Artist, civil engineer, inventor. Artist of merit and an experimenter in submarine mines and torpedoes; painted the first panorama ever shown in Paris. Achieved great distinction for the adaptation of steam power as a means of naval propulsion and for the design of the first successful steamboat, the *Clermont*.

NEG. NO. 35037

NEG. NO. 35038

JAMES ABRAM GARFIELD, 1831–1881, Ohio
Charles H. Niehaus, 1884-85 marble, 7'7"
Signed l. base Niehaus, sculptor
Rotunda

Soldier, lawyer, educator, statesman and President of
the U.S. Professor and later President of Hiram College,
1857–1861; member of the State senate 1859; Major
General in the Union Army, Civil War; Member of the
U.S. House of Representatives 1863–80; President 1881;
assassinated 5 months after his inauguration.

JAMES Z. GEORGE, 1826–1897, Mississippi
Signed r. base Augustus Lukeman, Sc., 1928;
   bronze, 7'8"
Hall of Columns

Lawyer, soldier in the War with Mexico and Confederate Brigadier General of the Civil War. Attained distinction as chief justice of the State supreme court 1879 and
as a U.S. Senator 1881–97; a leading member of the
Mississippi constitutional convention in 1890.

241

NEG. NO. 35039

GEORGE WASHINGTON GLICK, 1827–1911, Kansas
Charles H. Niehaus, 1913–14, marble, 7′5″
Signed r. base C. H. Niehaus
Hall of Columns

Lawyer, farmer, statesman and Governor of Kansas. A soldier in the Union Army in the Civil War; served 14 years in the State legislature. He was an uncompromising free-State man, and helped to prepare the constitution upon which the State of Kansas was admitted to the Union.

NEG. NO. 27494

JOHN GORRIE, 1803–1855, Florida
C. Adrian Pillars, marble, 7′6″
Signed r. base C. A. Pillars, 1913
Statuary Hall

Eminent physician and held the first patent on mechanical refrigeration which he developed to alleviate the suffering of the sick. This later led to discoveries of air conditioning and mechanical ice-making.

242

NATHANAEL GREENE, 1742–1786, Rhode Island
Henry Kirke Brown, marble, 6'4''
Signed top r. base H. K. Brown, 1869
East Central Hall

Deputy, General Assembly 1770–72, 1775; Major
General 1776 in the Revolutionary War; was engaged in
many major campaigns; acclaimed the "Savior of the
South". His was the first statue to be placed in Statuary
Hall 1870.

JOHN CAMPBELL GREENWAY, 1872–1926, Arizona
Signed top base Gutzon Borglum, 1928; bronze,
   8'2''
Statuary Hall

Distinguished soldier in the War with Spain; a member
of the Rough Riders; served in World War I with distinction; commissioned Brigadier General in 1922; noted
mining engineer and inventor of the turbo log washer.

HANNIBAL HAMLIN, 1809–1891, Maine
Signed top base Charles E. Tefft, 1933; bronze,
  6'8''

Statuary Hall

Statesman, U.S. House of Representatives 1843–47;
U.S. Senate 1848–57, and resigned to become Governor
of Maine 1857. Reelected to U.S. Senate 1857–61;
elected Vice President under Lincoln 1861–65. Enlisted
as private in the Maine State Guard, Civil War 1864;
collector of port of Boston; U.S. Senate 1869–81; U.S.
Minister to Spain 1881–82, when he resigned to devote
the remainder of his life to agricultural pursuits.

WADE HAMPTON, 1818–1902, South Carolina
Frederic W. Ruckstull, marble, 7'6''
Signed r. base F. W. RUCKSTULL· FECIT·
  1929·

House connecting corridor

Soldier, statesman, lawyer, Governor. Member of the
State senate 1858–62; served in the Confederate Army
commanding "Hampton's Legion"; rose to rank of
Lieutenant General commanded the Cavalry of the
Army of Northern Virginia; Governor of South Carolina
1876–79; and U.S. Senator 1879–91.

JOHN HANSON, 1715–1783, Maryland
Signed l. base Richard E. Brooks, Sc., Paris
MCMII [1902]; bronze, 7′9″
Senate connecting corridor

Patriot and statesman; first President under the Articles of Confederation; patriot of the Revolution; member of State house of delegates 9 terms; member of State senate 1757–73; delegate to General Congress in Annapolis 1774; member of the Continental Congress 1780–83; signer of the Articles of Confederation 1781.

JAMES HARLAN, 1820–1899, Iowa
Nellie V. Walker, bronze, 8′4″
Signed l. base N. V. Walker, 1909
Hall of Columns

Distinguished statesman, educator and orator. Principal of Iowa City College; State Superintendent of Public Instruction; President of Iowa Wesleyan College 1853–55. Secretary of the Interior 1865–66 under Andrew Johnson; U.S. Senator 1855–73; presiding judge on the Alabama Claims Commission. His daughter married Robert Todd Lincoln.

245

SAMUEL HOUSTON, 1793–1863, Texas
Signed l. base Elisabet Ney, fec., Austin,
  Texas, 1904; marble, 6'10"
Statuary Hall

Soldier, statesman, Governor. Served in the Creek
War 1818; commander in chief of the Texas Army.
Lawyer, district attorney and adjutant general of Tenn.
1820; U.S. House of Representatives from Tenn. 1823–
27; Governor of Tenn. 1827–29; first President of Republic of Texas 1841–44; took first steps toward annexation of Texas; Senator from Texas 1856–59;
Governor of Texas 1859–61; deposed when he refused
to take the oath of allegiance to the Confederate States.

JOHN J. INGALLS, 1833–1900, Kansas
Charles H. Niehaus, 1903–04 marble, 7'5"
Signed r. base C. H. Niehaus
Statuary Hall

Lawyer, scholar, orator and statesman. Delegate to
the Kansas constitutional convention; secretary of the
Kansas Territorial Council; member of the State
senate; secretary of state and served as judge advocate
during the Civil War, rising to the rank of lieutenant
colonel. Member of the U.S. Senate 1873–91.

KING KAMEHAMEHA I, c. 1758–1819, Hawaii
Thomas R. Gould, bronze, 8'7''
Signed back of base T. R. Gould, Inv. Et. Fecit,
   Florence 1879. Cast in 1968 from the original
Statuary Hall

Beloved leader who became King by virtue of his
ability to unite the warring islands under one government. Ruled wisely and well 1782–1819, encouraged
peaceful activities of agriculture and fishing and engaged in brisk trade from the time of Capt. Cook's
visit. The flag design he ordered for his kingdom has
become the symbol of the State of Hawaii.

ANDREW JACKSON, 1767–1845, Tennessee
Signed back of base Belle Kinney — L— F—
   Scholz, New York 1927; bronze, 7'6''
Rotunda

Lawyer, judge, soldier and 7th President of the U.S.
Courier in the Revolution at age 13; U.S. Representative
1796–97; Judge of Tenn. Supreme Court 1798–1804;
Creek War 1813; led the defeat of the British at New
Orleans 1815; captured Florida 1817 and became its
Governor 1821; U.S. Senate 1823–25; President 1829–37.

NEG. NO. 35049

NEG. NO. 28004

PHILIP KEARNY, 1814–1862, New Jersey
Henry Kirke Brown, bronze, 6'6''
Signed r. base H. K. Brown, Sculpt 1873
Hall of Columns

"The Perfect Soldier" who was distinguished on two continents for his conspicuous bravery and military accomplishments. He fought in Algiers 1840; in the War with Mexico 1848; and was Major General in the Civil War. He lost his life at Chantilly, Virginia, 1862.

JOHN E. KENNA, 1848–1893, West Virginia
Alexander Doyle, executed 1897–1901, marble
7'8''
Hall of Columns

Soldier, lawyer, statesman, enlisted in the Confederate Army in 1864 and was wounded in action; elected prosecuting attorney Kanawha County, 1872–1877; judge pro tem, circuit court of his home county, 1875; Member of the U.S. House of Representatives, 1877–1883; U.S. Senator 1883 until his death.

248

THOMAS STARR KING, 1824–1864, California
Signed front base Haig Patigian, 1930; bronze,
    7'2"
Hall of Columns

Preacher, patriot, orator; ordained a minister when
22 years old; received a call in 1860 to the First Unitarian
Church of California. During his 4 years service in San
Francisco he was a dominant factor in the support of the
Union. His portrait hangs in the capitol at Sacramento.
It bears this inscription:

"The man whose matchless oratory saved California
to the Union."

WILLIAM KING, 1768–1852, Maine
Signed r. base Franklin Simmons, Fecit 1877;
    marble, 7'5"
House connecting corridor

Statesman, Governor, industrialist. Member of the
Massachusetts legislature; assisted in securing passage of
the Act of Toleration and the Betterment Act (the first
step toward religious enfranchisement); Major General
of the Maine Militia in the War of 1812. Leader in
separating Maine from Massachusetts; President of
Maine constitutional convention, 1819; elected first
Governor of Maine in 1820.

FATHER EUSEBIO FRANCISCO KINO, S.J., 1645–
1711, Arizona
Signed l. base Suzanne Silvercruys 1964; bronze,
7'8"
Hall of Columns

A native of Italy and a contemporary of LaSalle and
Marquette; spent over 30 years in the Southwest as a
Jesuit missionary, explorer, cartographer, astronomer,
builder, historian and agriculturist; founded a chain of
24 missions and 19 ranches and made 14 expeditions into
the land which is now Arizona; began the cattle industry
in 3 places, planted fruit trees and introduced new grains.

SAMUEL JORDAN KIRKWOOD, 1813–1894, Iowa
Signed r. base Vinnie Ream; executed 1913,
bronze, 7'4"
Statuary Hall

Lawyer by profession, served as county prosecuting
attorney, 1845–49; member of the Ohio constitutional
convention, 1850–51; Iowa State senate, 1856–59;
Governor, 1860–64, 1876–77; U.S. Senator, 1866–67,
1877–81; Secretary of the Interior under President
Garfield, 1881–82.

250

NEG. NO. 35033

NEG. NO. 35054

ROBERT M. LA FOLLETTE, SR., 1855–1925,
   Wisconsin

Signed r. base Jo Davidson 1928; marble, 6'6"
Statuary Hall

Lawyer, statesman, Governor; was district attorney,
Dane County, 1880–84; Member of the United States
House of Representatives, 1885–1891; Governor of
Wisconsin, 1901–1906; resigned on election to the
United States Senate where he served from 1906 until his
death in 1925. He wrote into the law of the land many
constructive measures designed to safeguard the liberties
and economic interest of the workers.

REVEREND JASON LEE, 1803–1845, Oregon
Gifford MacG. Proctor, bronze, 6'11"
Signed l. back top of base G. MacG. Proctor 1952
Statuary Hall

Educator, missionary; orphaned at 3, self-supporting
at 13; educated in Mass. for the ministry; became the
first missionary in Oregon territory 1834; petitioned
Congress in 1838 to "take formal and speedy possession"
of the Oregon country.

251

ROBERT R. LIVINGSTON, 1746–1813, New York
Erastus Dow Palmer, bronze, 6'4''
Signed r. base E. D. Palmer, Sc., 1874
East Central Hall

ROBERT E. LEE, 1807–1870, Virginia
Signed l. base Edward V. Valentine, Sc.;
　executed 1909, bronze, 6'6''
Statuary Hall

A graduate of West Point, 1829 and superintendent, 1852, famed Confederate General of the Civil War. Following his heroic surrender to General Grant at Appomattox, he became President of Washington College at Lexington, Virginia, now named Washington and Lee University in his honor. He also served in the War with Mexico, 1847.

Jurist, diplomat, statesman. Delegate to the Continental Congress, 1775–77, 1779–81; one of committee of 5 who drafted the Declaration of Independence, but did not sign it; Delegate to State Constitutional Convention, 1777; Secretary of Foreign Affairs under the Articles of Confederation. As Chancellor of N.Y. State, he administered the first Presidential oath of office to George Washington, 1789; U.S. Minister to France, 1801–04, aided in negotiating the Louisiana Purchase; assisted Robert Fulton and his partner in constructing the first steamboat.

DR. CRAWFORD WILLIAMSON LONG, 1815–1878,
Georgia
J. Massey Rhind, 1924–25, marble, 7'2''
Signed front base Massey Rhind, Sc.
East Central Hall

Physician, humanitarian; first surgeon to use sul-
phuric ether as an anesthesia in 1842, considered one of
the great events in the history of surgery.

HUEY PIERCE LONG, 1893–1935, Louisiana
Signed r. back top Charles Keck, Sc.; executed
1938–40, bronze, 6'8''
Statuary Hall

Lawyer, State railroad commissioner; Governor of La.,
1928–1932; U.S. Senator, 1932–1935. He fostered the
distribution of free school books and equalized educational opportunities throughout Louisiana.

253

PERE JACQUES MARQUETTE, 1637–1675,
Wisconsin

Gaetano Trentanove, marble, 7'7''

Signed r. base Prof. G. Trentanove, Sculptor,
Florence, Italy; executed 1895

House connecting corridor

Pioneer explorer and missionary; French Jesuit missionary priest among the Indians of the northern country; his missions at Sault Ste. Marie and Mackinaw became the first towns in Michigan; explored the Miss. River and died on the return trip in 1675. Because he was neither a native nor a citizen of Wisconsin, the right of that State to commemorate him was established by a joint resolution of Congress Oct. 21, 1893.

PATRICK ANTHONY McCARRAN, 1876–1954
Nevada

Signed r. back top of base Yolande Jacobson,
1959; bronze, 7'3''

Statuary Hall vestibule north

Distinguished lawyer and statesman whose opinions as Chief Justice of the Nevada supreme court, 1917–1918, remain valued legal text; elected to the U.S. Senate in 1932, and served until his death in 1954.

NEG. NO. 35059

NEG. NO. 35060

DR. EPHRAIM MCDOWELL, 1771–1830, Kentucky
Charles H. Niehaus, bronze, 7'4''
Signed r. base C. H. Niehaus, Sculptor, 1928
Senate connecting corridor

A renowned physician, attended the University of Edinburgh, Scotland; successfully performed the first operation known as Ovariotomy in 1809; one of the founders and original trustees of Centre College, Danville, Kentucky; and a member of many medical societies.

DR. JOHN MCLOUGHLIN, 1784–1857, Oregon
Signed top base Gifford Proctor, Sc., 1952;
    bronze, 6'11''
House connecting corridor

Often called "the Father of Oregon"; was head of the powerful Hudson's Bay Company in the Pacific Northwest territory, 1824–1845; assisted the missionaries and settlers in what is now Washington and Oregon. His mild and just paternalistic rule aided the pioneers of the region to govern themselves and pass peacefully from British rule to American territorial status.

255

ESTHER HOBART MORRIS, 1813/14–1902, Wyoming
Signed l. base Avard Fairbanks, 1958; bronze, 8'
Statuary Hall vestibule north

Judge; mother of woman suffrage in Wyoming, was a convincing proponent and advocate of laws granting voting and office holding privileges to the women of the Wyoming territory; first woman to hold the office of justice of the peace, and no decision of hers was ever reversed by appeal to a higher court.

J. STERLING MORTON, 1832–1902, Nebraska
Rudulph Evans, 1936–37, bronze, 6'9"
Signed r. base R. Evans, Sc
Hall of Columns

A prominent statesman; leader in the early history of Nebraska; Secretary of the Nebraska Territory and acting Governor, 1858–1859; Secretary of Agriculture under President Cleveland, 1893, and originator of Arbor Day.

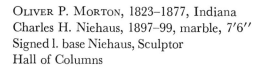

JOHN PETER GABRIEL MUHLENBERG, 1746–1807
Pennsylvania

Signed l. base Blanche Nevin, 1884; marble,
6′6″

Small House rotunda

Soldier, clergyman, statesman. Clergyman in Lutheran and Episcopal churches; member of Virginia House of Burgesses, 1774; Major General in Revolutionary War; Vice President of Pennsylvania Supreme Executive Council, 1785–1787; member of Pennsylvania constitutional convention 1790; member of U.S. House of Representatives, 1789–1791; 1793–1795; 1799–1801; member of U.S. Senate, 1801; Supervisor of Revenue for Pennsylvania, 1801; collector of Customs, 1802.

OLIVER P. MORTON, 1823–1877, Indiana
Charles H. Niehaus, 1897–99, marble, 7′6″
Signed l. base Niehaus, Sculptor
Hall of Columns

Served as circuit court judge, Indiana; Lt. Governor; Civil War governor who supported Lincoln and the Union cause; member of the U.S. Senate, 1867–77.

FRANCIS H. PIERPONT, 1814–1899, West Virginia
Signed l. base Franklin Simmons, 1903; marble,
7′7″
Statuary Hall

Patriot, statesman, Governor. Chosen Provisional
Governor of Virginia in 1861 by a staunch Union convention when state officials declared support for the
Confederacy; served as elected Governor of Virginia
1863–68; led the severance movement in western Virginia which resulted in the creation of West Virginia as
an independent state in 1863.

HENRY MOWER RICE, 1817–1894, Minnesota
Frederick E. Triebel, 1913–16, marble, 7′7″
Signed r. base Prof. F. E. Triebel, Sculptor,
College Point, New York
Statuary Hall

Businessman, statesman; was instrumental in securing
Minnesota Statehood; a delegate from the Territory;
later U.S. Senator 1853–63; appointed U.S. Commissioner to negotiate Indian Treaties, 1887–88.

CAESAR RODNEY, 1728–1784, Delaware
Signed r. base Bryant Baker, Sc., 1932; marble,
   7'5''

East Central Hall

Patriot, jurist; Delegate to the Stamp Act Congress; signer of the Declaration of Independence; a Member of the Continental Congress; Major General in the Revolutionary War; was in command at the Battle of Trenton; President of Delaware, 1778–1782; and occupied many positions of note in his native State.

WILL ROGERS, 1879–1935, Oklahoma
Signed r. base Jo Davidson, Paris, 1938; bronze,
   7'6''

House connecting corridor

Humorist, humanitarian, cowboy, showman, comedian (stage, screen, and radio), actor, author, after-dinner speaker, columnist, commentator, philosopher, world traveler, goodwill ambassador.

URIAH M. ROSE, 1834–1913, Arkansas
Frederic W. Ruckstuhl, marble, 7'6''
Signed r. base F. W. Ruckstuhl, Fecit, 1917
Statuary Hall

Lawyer of international reputation; chancellor of the State; charter member of American Bar Association and its president in 1901; authored the "Arkansas Constitution" and "Digest of Arkansas Reports"; appointed by Theodore Roosevelt in 1907 as one of the delegates to the Peace Congress of The Hague with the rank of ambassador.

CHARLES MARION RUSSELL, 1864–1926, Montana
John B. Weaver, 1957–58, bronze, 7'1''
Signed back of base Jack Weaver, Sculptor
Statuary Hall

Known as "The Cowboy Artist," was an illustrator, writer, philosopher, and humorist who faithfully and devotedly recorded the spirit of the Old West.

NEG. NO. 35069

DR. FLORENCE RENA SABIN, 1871–1953, Colorado
Signed l. side of chair Joy Flinsch Buba 1958;
    bronze, 5'3''
Statuary Hall

Distinguished teacher, scientist, humanitarian and
writer of medical texts; pioneered woman membership
into the National Academy of Sciences and entrance
into Johns Hopkins Medical School; faculty member of
the Rockefeller Institute of Medical Research; she was
instrumental in the drafting and enacting of the *Sabin
Health Laws* in Colorado.

NEG. NO. 35070

MARIA L. SANFORD, 1836–1920, Minnesota
Signed l. base Evelyn Raymond 1958; bronze,
    6'11''
Senate connecting corridor

Noted woman orator and educator—one of the first
women professors in the U.S.; leader in adult education;
founder of early parent-teacher groups; espoused
education for Negroes, justice for the Indians, and
women's rights.

261

NEG. NO. 35071

NEG. NO. 35072

Sequoya, 1770–1845, Oklahoma
Signed r. base Vinnie Ream/G. J. Zolnay;
    executed 1917, bronze, 7′6″
Statuary Hall

Cherokee leader, skilled as a silversmith, blacksmith, philosopher, trader, but famous because he developed the 86 character alphabet for the Cherokee Nation 1821, thus giving his people a written language. Sent to Washington as a delegate from Western Cherokees 1828; Anglicized name was George Guess.

Junipero Serra, 1713–1784, California
Ettore Cadorin, 1930, bronze, 8′9″
Signed r. base E. Cadorin
Statuary Hall

Missionary, pioneer of pioneers; founder and moving spirit of 9 California missions between 1769–84, during his presidency of the Franciscan friars.

262

GENERAL EDMUND KIRBY SMITH, 1824–1893,
   Florida
Charles A. Pillars, bronze, 7′5″
Signed r. base C. A. Pillars, SC. 1917
Hall of Columns

   Soldier-educator; graduated with honors from West
Point, served in the War with Mexico and was a General
in the Confederate Army; Chancellor of the University
of Nashville; taught mathematics at West Point, 1849–52,
and the University of Sewanee (Tenn.).

JOHN STARK, 1728–1822, New Hampshire
Carl Conrads, 1894, marble, 6′5″
Vestibule north of Rotunda

   Patriot and soldier; a courageous and relentless soldier
during the French and Indian War, 1754–1763; led
Washington's advance at Trenton, 1776; headed the
New Hampshire troops at the Battle of Bunker Hill,
1775; and won the Battle of Bennington, 1777; commissioned a Major General in 1786.

ALEXANDER HAMILTON STEPHENS, 1812–1883,
  Georgia
Gutzon Borglum, marble 5′8″, executed 1926–
  27
Statuary Hall

   Lawyer, U.S. Representative 1843–59; elected to the
Confederate Congress and chosen vice president of the
provisional government of the Confederacy, 1861–65;
was elected to the U.S. Senate after the war but was
denied admission; author of *The War Between the States;*
U.S. House of Representatives, 1873–82; Governor of
Georgia, 1882–83.

RICHARD STOCKTON, 1730–1781, New Jersey
Henry Kirke Brown, marble, 6′3″
Signed front base H. K. Brown, 1874
East Central Hall

   Lawyer, jurist and signer of the Declaration of
Independence; an associate justice on the New Jersey
supreme court, 1774–1776; a member of the Continental
Congress, 1776.

JONATHAN TRUMBULL, 1710–1785, Connecticut
Chauncey B. Ives, marble, 8'1"
Signed r. base C. B. Ives, Fecit, Romae, 1869
House connecting corridor

Soldier, statesman and minister; espoused the cause of independence, aided General Washington, and worked for a stronger Union; one of the outstanding figures of Connecticut commerce, served in the Connecticut Assembly; Governor 15 years; State's chief justice in colonial times, 1769–1784; father of the artist John Trumbull.

ZEBULON BAIRD VANCE, 1830–1894, North
 Carolina
Signed top base Gutzon Borglum, 1916; bronze,
 7'8"
Statuary Hall

Soldier, lawyer, statesman. Member of the State house of commons, 1854; Member of the U.S. House of Representatives, 1858–1861; entered the Confederate Army during the Civil War as a captain, 1861; promoted to a Colonel; twice Governor of North Carolina, served in the U.S. Senate, 1879–1894.

NEG. NO. 35081

NEG. NO. 35082

GENERAL LEW WALLACE, 1827–1905, Indiana
Andrew O'Connor, marble, 6'10", executed
1908–09
Signed r. base A. O'Connor
Statuary Hall

Successful as lawyer, soldier, diplomat, and author; served in the War with Mexico; Major General during the Civil War; served in the Indiana State senate, as territorial Governor of New Mexico and Minister to Turkey; authored the classic novel, *Ben Hur* one of the best sellers of all time.

JOSEPH WARD, 1838–1889, South Dakota
Signed r. base Bruno Beghé, Sculptor; executed
1963, marble, 7'2"
Hall of Columns

Educator, churchman, and statesman; organized Yankton Academy, 1872; founded Yankton College, 1881; drafted a code of school laws for the Dakota Territory; served in the Union Army; ordained a missionary, 1869; the "father of Congregationalism" in the Dakotas. Outstanding leader in the struggle for South Dakota Statehood; author of State Constitution as adopted; composed the state motto, "Under God the people rule," and the Great Seal of South Dakota is the result for his written description for this emblem.

NEG. NO. 35083

NEG. NO. 35084

GEORGE WASHINGTON, 1732–1799, Virginia
Antoine Houdon, bronze, 7'6''; 1909 casting
  from the original 1788 marble
Rotunda

Statesman, patriot, soldier, surveyor, first President
of the United States; commander in chief of the Colonial
forces; President of the Constitutional Convention;
delegate to the First and Second Constitutional Con-
gresses.

DANIEL WEBSTER, 1782–1852, New Hampshire
Carl Conrads, executed 1893–94, marble, 6'4''
Statuary Hall

Constitutional lawyer, orator and statesman; Represented his native State, New Hampshire in the U.S.
House of Representatives, 1813–1817; represented his
adopted State of Massachusetts in the House, 1823–
1827 and in the U.S. Senate, 1827–1841 and 1845–
1850. Secretary of State under Presidents Harrison,
Tyler and Fillmore.

269

NEG. NO. 35085

NEG. NO. 35086

GENERAL JOSEPH WHEELER, 1836–1906, Alabama

Berthold Nebel, executed 1923–25, bronze, 7′

Signed l. back top of base B. Nebel

Statuary Hall

Soldier, lawyer, graduate of West Point, served in the Confederate Army and attained the rank of senior cavalry officer; served in the Army during the War with Spain and was made brigadier general; a Representative in Congress eighteen years.

EDWARD DOUGLASS WHITE, 1845–1921, Louisiana

Signed top r. side of base Arthur Morgan, Sculptor, 1954; bronze, 7′1″

Senate connecting corridor

Noted jurist, and statesman; at 16 he became a soldier in the Confederate Army; Member of State senate, 1874–1878; associate justice of the State supreme court, 1879–1880; elected U.S. Senator, 1891–1894; appointed Associate Justice of the Supreme Court of the U.S., 1894; Chief Justice of the U.S., 1910–1921.

270

NEG. NO. 35087

NEG. NO. 35088

Marcus Whitman, 1802–1847, Washington
Signed l. base Avard Fairbanks, 1950; bronze,
  9′
Statuary Hall

Pioneer, doctor, missionary, farmer; courageous medical missionary in the Washington Territory; in 1836 he led a party to the Oregon Territory and settled near the present city of Walla Walla, Washington; assisted the "Great Emigration" of 1843, the first large movement of settlers to the northwest. He and his wife Narcissa, were massacred by the Indians in 1847.

Frances E. Willard, 1839–1898, Illinois
Signed l. base Helen Farnsworth Mears,
  Fecit, MCMV [1905]; marble, 7′1″
Statuary Hall

Educator, social and economic reformer, orator and journalist; president of Evanston College for Ladies, 1871 (later part of Northwestern University); dean and professor of aesthetics at Northwestern; associated in evangelist movement with Dwight Moody, 1873; elected president of National Woman's Temperance Union, 1879; founder and president of World's Christian Temperance Union, 1883.

271

ROGER WILLIAMS, 1603–1682/83, Rhode Island
Signed l. base Franklin Simmons, Sculptor,
    Rome, 1870; marble, 6'8''
Hall of Columns

Colonizer, minister, founder of Rhode Island. Born
in England, came to America, 1631; pastor of the
Puritan Church at Salem, Mass. Banished from the
Massachusetts colony in 1635: founded Rhode Island,
1636, and secured the charter for the Providence
Plantations, 1644; author of the great declaration of the
principle of religious liberty and freedom in the organization of the State; his statue was the second to be
placed in Statuary Hall, 1872.

JOHN WINTHROP, 1588–1649, Massachusetts
Signed l. base Richard S. Greenough, Sculpsit,
    1875; marble, 7'8''
Hall of Columns

Puritan colonizer, author, lawyer; first Governor of
Massachusetts Bay Colony, and served 12 years; believed
in evangelizing the Indians; opposed democracy, and
believed superior minds, though always in the minority,
should rule.

BRIGHAM YOUNG, 1801–1877, Utah
Mahonri Young, marble, 5′11″
Signed r. base Mahonri, 1947
Statuary Hall

 Pioneer, empire builder; led the Mormon pioneers to Salt Lake Valley in 1847; preeminent in the settling and establishing of the Territory of Deseret, now the State of Utah; and was one of the Territory's most illustrious Governors; President of The Church of Jesus Christ of Latter-day Saints 1844–1877.

273

NEG. NO. 35092

NEG. NO. 26687

EDWARD DICKINSON BAKER, 1811–1861
Horatio Stone, marble, 6′5″
Purchase authorized 1873, Stats. L., v. 17, p. 513
Rotunda

U.S. Representative from Illinois 1845–46; served in Mexican and Civil Wars; Senator from Oregon from 1860 until October 21, 1861, when he was killed at Balls Bluff, Virginia, while serving as a major general in the Union Army.

BENJAMIN FRANKLIN, 1706–1790
Signed r. base H. Powers, Sculp, 1862; marble, 7′11″
Contract for purchase 1859; placed 1862
Senate wing, second floor, east corridor

GENERAL ULYSSES S. GRANT, 1822–1885
Signed l. base Franklin Simmons, Fecit 1899;
    marble, 7'5''
Gift from Grand Army of the Republic, 1890
Accepted by Public Res. 39, 51st Congress
Rotunda

ALEXANDER HAMILTON, 1757–1804
Signed r. base Horatio Stone, Fac Rome 1868;
    marble, 7'9''
Purchased 1866–68; placed 1868
Rotunda

NEG. NO. 26688

NEG. NO. 35098

THOMAS JEFFERSON, 1743–1826
Signed r. base P. J. David D'angers, Sculp. 1833;
  bronze, 7′6″
Gift of Lt. Uriah P. Levy USN, 1833
Rotunda

By resolution placed in Rotunda 1834 for about a year, then moved to the north grounds of the White House; returned to the Capitol in 1874 and formally accepted by resolution of March 18, 1874.

JOHN HANCOCK, 1737–1793
Signed r. base Horatio Stone, Sculp't 1861;
  marble, 7′6″
Purchased 1857–61
Senate wing, second floor, west corridor

276

NEG. NO. 26348

NEG. NO. 35099

THOMAS JEFFERSON, 1743–1826
Signed l. side of column H. Powers, Sculp 1863; marble, 8′
Purchased by contract 1859; placed 1863
House wing, second floor, east corridor

ABRAHAM LINCOLN, 1809–1865
Signed r. base Vinnie Ream, 1870; marble, 6′ 11″
Purchased 1871
Rotunda

277

SAM RAYBURN, 1882–1961
Signed top r. base Felix de Weldon, Sc. 1965; bronze, 6′
Gift of Texas State Society of Washington, D.C., 1965
Accepted by House Office Building Commission, 1964
Rayburn House Office Building, main entrance

Representative from Texas 1913–1961.

STATUE OF LIBERTY AND THE EAGLE

In the niche above the entablature on the south wall of Statuary Hall stands the heroic-sized figure of Liberty. Placed there between 1817–1819 when the Capitol was rebuilt after the fire of 1814, she originally looked down on the House of Representatives which met in the Hall. Her right hand, extending over the American eagle, holds the Constitution of the United States. At her left is the frustum of a column serving as an altar around which the serpent, the emblem of wisdom, is entwined.

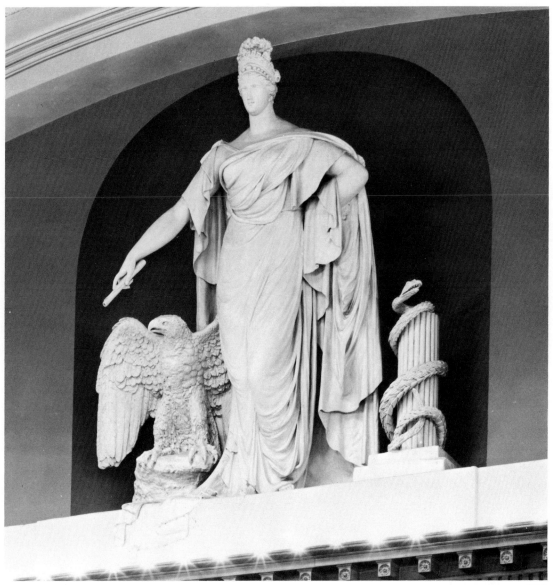

NEG. NO. 35101

LIBERTY AND THE EAGLE
Enrico Causici, plaster, 13'7"
Statuary Hall

MEMORIAL TO THE PIONEERS OF THE WOMEN'S SUFFRAGE MOVEMENT

This portrait monument was accepted as a gift from the women of the United States, through the National Woman's Party, by the Joint Committee on the Library, February 15, 1921. The original block of marble from which these busts were carved measured 7′ x 5′ 8″ x 5′, and the estimated weight is between 7 and 8 tons.

In accepting the monument the Joint Committee on the Library directed that it be placed temporarily "in the Rotunda for the purpose of appropriate ceremonies of tender and reception and at the conclusion of the ceremonies, the said sculpture be placed in the Crypt on the first floor of the Capitol beneath the Dome." It was moved from the Rotunda to the Crypt May 1921.

NEG. NO. 33706

ELIZABETH CADY STANTON (1815–1902), 26″
Susan B. Anthony (1820–1906), 35″
Lucretia Mott (1793–1880), 24″
Signed r. side Adelaide Johnson, 1921; and l.r. on back A.J.
Crypt, first floor

Reliefs

House Chamber
Old Supreme Court Chamber
Rotunda
Senate Chamber
East Central Portico

RELIEFS IN THE HOUSE CHAMBER

LAWGIVERS

The 23 relief portraits in marble are of men noted in history for the part they played in the evolution of what has become American law. They were placed over the gallery doors of the House of Representatives Chamber when it was remodeled 1949–50.

Created in bas relief of white Vermont marble by seven different sculptors, the plaques each measure 28″ in diameter. One is full face, and 22 are profile. From the full face of Moses on the north wall, 11 profiles face left and 11 face right, ending at the Webster quotation on the south wall above the Speaker's chair. (See page 398.)

The subjects of the plaques were jointly chosen by a group from the University of Pennsylvania, and the Columbia Historical Society of Washington, D.C. in consultation with authoritative staff members of the Library of Congress. The selection was approved by a special committee of five Members of the House of Representatives, the Architect of the Capitol and his associates.

The plaster models of these reliefs may be seen on the walls of the Rayburn House Office Building subway terminal.

In chronological order the lawgivers are:

Hammurabi	c 2067–2025 B.C.	St. Louis	1214–1270 A.D.
Moses	c 1571–1451 B.C.	Alphonso X	1221–1284 A.D.
Lycurgus	c 900 B.C.	Edward I	1239–1307 A.D.
Solon	c 594 B.C.	Suleiman	1494–1566 A.D.
Gaius	c 110–180 A.D.	Grotius	1583–1645 A.D.
Papinian	c 200 A.D.	Colbert	1619–1683 A.D.
Justinian	c 483–565 A.D.	Pothier	1699–1772 A.D.
Tribonian	c 500–547 A.D.	Blackstone	1723–1780 A.D.
Maimonides	c 1135–1204 A.D.	Mason	1726–1792 A.D.
Gregory IX	c 1147–1241 A.D.	Jefferson	1743–1826 A.D.
Innocent III	1161–1216 A.D.	Napoleon	1769–1821 A.D.
de Montfort	1200–1265 A.D.		

The accompanying illustrations are arranged alphabetically.

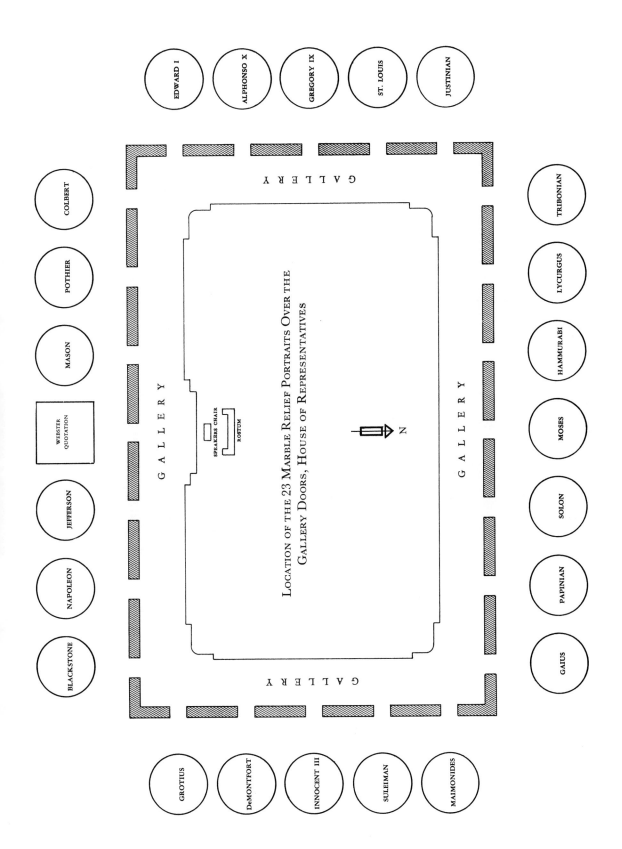

LOCATION OF THE 23 MARBLE RELIEF PORTRAITS OVER THE GALLERY DOORS, HOUSE OF REPRESENTATIVES

EDWARD I
ALPHONSO X
GREGORY IX
ST. LOUIS
JUSTINIAN

COLBERT
POTHIER
MASON
WEBSTER QUOTATION
JEFFERSON
NAPOLEON
BLACKSTONE

TRIBONIAN
LYCURGUS
HAMMURABI
MOSES
SOLON
PAPINIAN
GAIUS

GROTIUS
DeMONTFORT
INNOCENT III
SULEIMAN
MAIMONIDES

GALLERY

GALLERY

GALLERY

GALLERY

SPEAKERS CHAIR

ROSTUM

N

283

ALPHONSO X, THE "WISE," 1221–1284
Gaetano Cecere
Signed l.r. G. Cecere

King of Leon and Castile; author of the *Fuero Real*, a compilation of local legislation for general use; originator of the code, *Las Siete Partidas*, used as a basis for Spanish jurisprudence.

BLACKSTONE, 1723–1780
Thomas Hudson Jones
Signed l.r. T. H. Jones

Sir William Blackstone, celebrated English jurist; author of *Commentaries on the Laws of England*, which had considerable influence on the importation and adaptation of English common law in this country.

COLBERT, 1619–1683
Laura Gardin Fraser
Signed l.r. L. G. F.

Jean Baptiste Colbert, French statesman; codifier of ordinances; reformer of the French legal system.

DE MONTFORT, c. 1200–1265
Gaetano Cecere
Signed bottom center G. Cecere

Simon de Montfort, English statesman; advocate of representative government.

NEG. NO. 34065

NEG. NO. 34066

EDWARD I
Laura Gardin Fraser
Signed l.r. L. G. F.

King of England; eliminator of feudalism from political life; summoner of the "Model Parliament," which established the parliamentary constitution of England.

GAIUS, c. 110–180
Joseph Kiselewski

Celebrated Roman jurist; author of several works including the *Institutes*, a complete exposition of the elements of Roman law which became important sources of Roman civil law.

NEG. NO. 34067

NEG. NO. 34068

GREGORY IX, c. 1147–1241
Thomas Hudson Jones
Signed l.r. T. H. Jones

Author of a compilation of decretals on canon law, who accomplished much in maintaining the remnants of Roman law during a critical period.

GROTIUS, 1583–1645
C. Paul Jennewein

Hugo Grotius, Dutch statesman; Advocate-General of the provinces of Holland and Zeeland; author of *De jure qelli et pacis*, a fundamental doctrine of international law.

285

NEG. NO. 34069

HAMMURABI, reigned 2067–2025 B.C.
Thomas Hudson Jones
Signed l.r. T. H. Jones

King of Babylonia; author of a great law code bearing his name which is characterized by its primitiveness and recognized in legal literature as perhaps the earliest surviving code.

NEG. NO. 34070

INNOCENT III, 1161–1216
Joseph Kiselewski

Student of canon and civil law, who, like Gregory IX, preserved the remnants of Roman law during a dark and critical period of human history.

NEG. NO. 34071

JEFFERSON, 1743–1826
C. Paul Jennewein

Thomas Jefferson, third President of the United States; author of the Declaration of Independence and the Statute of Virginia for Religious Freedom.

NEG. NO. 34072

JUSTINIAN I, 483–565
Gaetano Cecere
Signed l.r. G. Cecere

Byzantine emperor who consolidated the pre-existing Roman law into two collections, the *Digest* or *Pandects* and the *Corpus Iuris Civilis.*

LYCURGUS, c. 900 B.C.

C. Paul Jennewein

Legislator, traditional author of laws and institutions of Sparta.

MAIMONIDES, 1135–1204

Brenda Putnam.

Jewish philosopher who compiled a systematic exposition of the whole of Jewish law as contained in the Pentateuch and in Talmudic literature.

MASON, 1725–1792

Gaetano Cecere

Signed l.r. G. Cecere

George Mason, drafter of the Virginia Constitution and Bill of Rights 1776; member of the Constitutional Convention in 1787; originator of several amendments later incorporated in the present Bill of Rights.

MOSES, c. 1571–1451 B.C.

Jean de Marco

Signed l.r. J. De Marco

Unexcelled Hebrew prophet and lawgiver who transformed an enslaved wandering people into a nation, disciplined and breathed into them character; received the Ten Commandments.

287

NEG. NO. 34077

Napoleon I, 1769–1821
C. Paul Jennewein
Signed l.l. C. P. Jennewein, Sc., 1950

Emperor of France who appointed a commission to draw up the *code civil*, a combination of tradition and Roman law which was quite influential on the legal systems of European and American states during the 19th century.

NEG. NO. 34087

Papinian, died c. 212
Laura Gardin Fraser

Roman jurist, remarkable for his juridical genius, independence of judgment, lucidity and firmness, and for his sense of right and morality by which he frequently rose above the barriers of national prejudices.

NEG. NO. 34079

Pothier, 1699–1772
Joseph Kiselewski

Robert Joseph Pothier, French jurist; author of *Pandectae Justinianae in novum ordinem digestae*, a classic in the study of Roman law; author of several treatises on French law, incorporated in the French Code Civil.

NEG. NO. 34080

Saint Louis, 1214–1270
Jean de Marco
Signed l.r. J. De Marco

(Louis IX) King of France; author of the *Mise of Amiens*.

288

SOLON, c. 638–558 B.C.
Brenda Putnam

Athenian statesman; author of constitutional and legal reforms.

SULEIMAN, 1494–1566
Joseph Kiselewski

Sultan of Turkey; reformed and improved civil and military codes and ameliorated the lot of his Christian subjects.

Tribonian, c. 500–547
Signed bottom center: Brenda Putnam, Sc., 1950

Byzantine jurist; head of the commission which compiled the laws under Justinian I.

289

STATE SEALS IN THE CEILING OF THE HOUSE OF REPRESENTATIVES

Upon the completion of the skylight of the chamber of the House of Representatives, stained glass seals of the 31 States and 4 possessions of the United States were installed in 1857–1858. These early seals were designed and painted by Johannes Adam Oertel. New seals were added as States were admitted to the Union, but the artists have not been documented.

During the remodeling of the House Chamber in 1949, the old cast iron ceiling with its glass skylights was replaced. The glass seals, which were about 21″ in diameter of double thick ornamental glass in iron frames, were given to the respective States.

New seals were reproduced from the original glass seals. They were cast in plaster and painted the appropriate colors.

In the center of the new ceiling there is a laylight, the field of which is of carved glass outlining the figure of an eagle, framed in bronze. It is illuminated artificially from above.

The seals of Hawaii and Alaska were added in 1962.

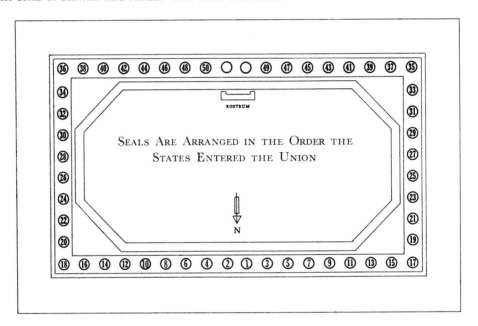

From the lower center reading to the left the seals are:

2	Pennsylvania	28	Texas
4	Georgia	30	Wisconsin
6	Massachusetts	32	Minnesota
8	South Carolina	34	Kansas
10	Virginia	36	Nevada
12	North Carolina	38	Colorado
14	Vermont	40	South Dakota
16	Tennessee	42	Washington
18	Louisiana	44	Wyoming
20	Mississippi	46	Oklahoma
22	Alabama	48	Arizona
24	Missouri	50	Hawaii
26	Michigan	0	Virgin Islands

From the lower center reading to the right the seals are:

1	Delaware	27	Florida
3	New Jersey	29	Iowa
5	Connecticut	31	California
7	Maryland	33	Oregon
9	New Hampshire	35	West Virginia
11	New York	37	Nebraska
13	Rhode Island	39	North Dakota
15	Kentucky	41	Montana
17	Ohio	43	Idaho
19	Indiana	45	Utah
21	Illinois	47	New Mexico
23	Maine	49	Alaska
25	Arkansas	0	Puerto Rico

RELIEF IN OLD SUPREME COURT CHAMBER

JUSTICE

This plaster relief is located in the chamber the Supreme Court used for 60 years. The appropriate relief of Justice was commissioned for the Court after the fire of 1814. A mythical figure of Justice is seated in the center of the lunette. In her left hand she holds the scales, and her right hand rests upon a sword. On the right is an eagle guarding the laws: on the left, a youthful winged figure—presumably typifying the Young Nation—crowned by the rising sun, is pointing to the Constitution of the United States. The background is light blue with accents of gold on the edges of the books, on the sun, the writing on the tablet, and on the scales.

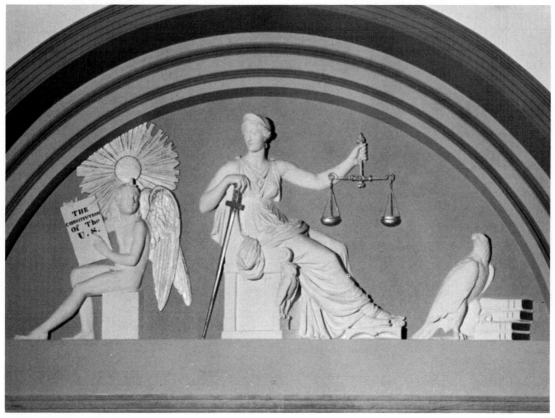

NEG. NO. 40194

JUSTICE
Carlo Franzoni, plaster, May 1817
S–141

RELIEFS IN THE ROTUNDA

Above each of the four Rotunda doors are scenes from the history of the American Colonies carved in relief into the sandstone walls. The three sculptors who decorated the Rotunda were employed during the rebuilding of the Capitol after the fire of 1814.

Between the historic scenes, decorative panels of wreaths and portraits, also in relief, circle the Rotunda walls.

NEG. NO. 24560

CONFLICT OF DANIEL BOONE AND THE INDIANS, 1773
Signed l.r. Enrico Causici of Verona, Fecit; 1826–27
Rotunda, above south door

NEG. NO. 24561

WILLIAM PENN'S TREATY WITH THE INDIANS, 1682
Nicholas Gevelot
Signed l.l. N. Gevelot, 1827
Rotunda, above north door

LANDING OF THE PILGRIMS, 1620
Signed l.r. Enrico Causici of Verona, Fecit, 1825
Rotunda, above east door

PRESERVATION OF CAPTAIN SMITH BY POCAHONTAS, 1606
Signed l.l. A. Capellano, Fecit, 1825
Rotunda, above west door

JOHN CABOT
Francisco Iardella, 1828
Above the painting "Landing of Columbus"

CHRISTOPHER COLUMBUS
Attributed to Francisco Iardella
Above the painting "Surrender of General Burgoyne"

295

RENÉ ROBERT CAVELIER SIEUR DE LA SALLE
Francisco Iardella, 1829
Above the painting "Discovery of the Mississippi River"

SIR WALTER RALEIGH
Attributed to Francisco Iardella
Above the painting "Surrender of Lord Cornwallis"

RELIEFS IN THE SENATE CHAMBER

Three marble panels, designed by sculptor Lee Lawrie, were placed above the entries to the Senate Chamber when it was remodeled 1949–50.

The plaster models of these panels are located on the walls of the Capitol terminal of the Senate subway.

NEG. NO. 24722

COURAGE
Lee Lawrie
Bruno Mankowski, carver
West entry

Courage, symbolizing our Nation, unflinchingly battles Evil, the serpent, and vanquishes it.

NEG. NO. 24720

PATRIOTISM
Lee Lawrie
Louis Milione, carver
East entry

Patriotism is depicted by a citizen leaning on his plow, a symbol of every man's usual work, which he leaves to take up the sword for the defense of his country. The strident eagle symbolizes Vigilance and Preparedness.

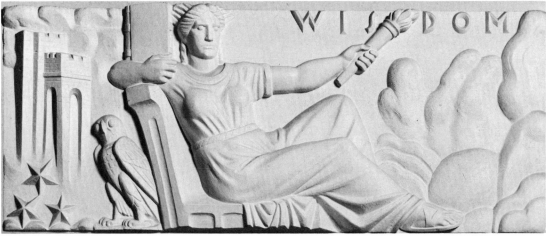

NEG. NO. 24721

WISDOM
Lee Lawrie
Edward H. Ratti, carver
South entry

Wisdom is represented by the figure of a woman, from whose head come rays of light. She holds a book symbolizing the experience of the ages, or the Laws. In the other hand she holds a torch which illuminates the sphere representing the earth. The tower on the left is her temple. The stars, earth and clouds suggest that Wisdom is above earthly derivation.

RELIEFS ON THE EAST CENTRAL PORTICO
FAME AND PEACE

Above the Rotunda bronze doors of the east portico is the relief "Fame and Peace Crowning Washington." The two winged figures, hovering in the air, crown the bust of George Washington with laurel wreaths. Fame, on the right, holds a trumpet, and Peace, on the left, a palm branch.

The original sandstone panel and bust were executed by Antonio Capellano in 1827. At the time of the Extension of the East Central Front of the Capitol, they were reproduced in marble by the carvers of the Vermont Marble Company, 1959–60.

The plaster model is located on the north wall of the Everett McKinley Dirksen Office Building subway terminal. The original bust is on display (see page 196), and the panel is in storage.

NEG. NO. 20418

FAME AND PEACE CROWNING GEORGE WASHINGTON
Antonio Capellano, 1827, 18′8″ x 5′¼″
G. Giannetti, models for the marble, 1959–60
East central portico

WREATH PANELS

Directly over the niches containing the statues of War and Peace on the portico of the east front are two panels in relief. In each panel thirteen arrows, symbolic of the Thirteen Original States, are embraced by leafed branches and fruit from the oak and pineapple.

According to available records, the original sandstone panels were carved by Thomas McIntosh and Jeremiah Sullivan about 1825. During the Extension of the East Central Front of the Capitol, the panels were reproduced in marble by carvers of the Vermont Marble Company, 1959–60.

The plaster model of the panels is located in the Everett McKinley Dirksen Office Building subway terminal. The original sandstone panels are in storage.

NEG. NO. 19159

DECORATIVE WREATH PANELS (2), model
Thomas McIntosh and Jeremiah Sullivan, 1825
G. Giannetti, models for the marble, 1959–60
East central portico

Frescoes and Murals

Rotunda

House Wing

Senate Wing

ROTUNDA

The focal point of the great Rotunda is the canopy of the dome where the fresco, "The Apotheosis of George Washington," may be seen 180 feet above the Rotunda floor. It is 62'2'' in diameter with a concavity of 20'7'' containing 4664 square feet. The figures, which appear life size to the viewer, are approximately 15 feet high. The cartoons or sketches were drawn in 1863 and the fresco, begun in 1864, was completed in about 11 months. It is signed C. Brumidi, 1865.

S. D. Wyeth, a writer of 1866, stated that the "great fresco picture by Brumidi arrests the gaze as though the sky had opened . . ."

It is an allegorical painting which combines mythological and historical figures. In the center, Washington apotheosized, is seated in majesty. On his right is the Goddess of Liberty and on his left is a winged figure, symbolic of Victory and Fame, sounding a trumpet. Surrounding Washington are thirteen maidens, symbolizing the original States, holding a banner emblazoned with the motto "E Pluribus Unum."

The border is composed of six allegorical groupings. Below Washington is *War*, with Freedom holding a shield and accompanied by the Eagle, striking down Tyranny and Kingly Power.

Continuing clockwise, *Art* and *Sciences* are represented by Minerva, Goddess of Wisdom, teaching Benjamin Franklin, Robert Fulton and Samuel F. B. Morse. Young boys listen and learn at her feet.

Marine, personified by Neptune bearing his trident, is accompanied by Venus, born of the Sea, holding in her hand the Atlantic Cable.

Commerce is represented by Mercury, Protector of Travelers and Merchants. He holds in his hand a bag of gold as he turns toward Robert Morris, financier of the American Revolution. The signature of Brumidi is found on a box at Morris' feet.

Mechanics, symbolized by Vulcan, rests his foot on a cannon and surrounding him are man-made products suggesting giant forces of nature can be subservient to human will.

Agriculture is represented by Ceres with a cornucopia. America, wearing a red liberty cap, is turning over to Ceres the mastery of a team of horses pulling a reaper. Flora gathers flowers and Pomona bears a basket of fruit.

APOTHEOSIS OF WASHINGTON
Constantino Brumidi, fresco, 1865
Canopy of the Dome

ROTUNDA FRIEZE

The frescoed frieze on the interior of the Rotunda is located 58′ above the floor. It is 300′ in circumference and 8′3″ high.

Constantino Brumidi created the designs and completed about one third of the frieze before his death in 1880.

> America in History
> Landing of Columbus, 1492
> Entry of Cortez into the Halls of Montezuma, 1521
> Pizarro's Conquest of Peru, 1533
> Midnight Burial of De Soto in the Mississippi, 1542
> Pocahontas Saving the Life of Capt. John Smith, 1607
> Landing of the Pilgrims at Plymouth, Mass., 1620
> Penn's Treaty with the Indians, 1682 (approximately half)

The work was continued by Filippo Costaggini. From 1880 to 1888 he used all the designs which Brumidi had prepared to complete the frieze. However, a 31′2″ gap in the design resulted and the frieze was left incomplete. Costaggini's work includes:

> Colonization of New England
> Peace Between Governor Oglethorpe and the Indians, 1732
> Battle of Lexington, 1775
> Reading of the Declaration of Independence, 1776
> Surrender of Cornwallis at Yorktown, 1781
> Death of Tecumseh at the Battle of Thames, 1813
> Entry of General Scott into the City of Mexico, 1847
> Discovery of Gold in California, 1848

Numerous legislative efforts to appropriate sufficient money and to find a suitable artist to complete the frieze were unsuccessful until 1950 when a resolution providing for completion was signed into law. The Joint Committee on the Library agreed that the unfinished area of the frieze should contain suitable scenes depicting:

> The Civil War [1865]
> The Spanish-American War [1898]
> The Birth of Aviation in the United States [1903]

Allyn Cox was engaged to complete these panels. Mr. Cox finished his painting in the summer of 1953, and that fall he cleaned and restored the original Brumidi-Costaggini work. The frieze was illuminated and dedicated with appropriate ceremonies on May 11, 1954.

ORIGINAL SKETCHES OF THE ROTUNDA FRIEZE

The original sketch for the Rotunda frieze, from which Constantino Brumidi made the larger cartoons, was presented to the Government by Mrs. Myrtle Cheney Murdock in 1961. It is preserved in the Office of the Architect of the Capitol.

304

ROTUNDA FRIEZE

America in History   Landing of Columbus, 1492   Entry of Cortez into the Halls of Montezuma, 1521   Pizarro's Conquest of Peru, 1533   Midnight Burial of De Soto in the Mississippi, 1542

Pocahontas Saving Life of Capt. John Smith, 1607   Landing of Pilgrims at Plymouth, Mass., 1620   Penn's Treaty With the Indians, 1682   Colonization of New England   Peace Between Governor Oglethorpe and the Indians, 1732

Battle of Lexington, 1775   Reading of the Declaration of Independence, 1776   Surrender of Cornwallis at Yorktown, 1781   Death of Tecumseh at the Battle of Thames, 1813

Entry of General Scott into the City of Mexico, 1847   Discovery of Gold in California, 1848   The Civil War, 1865   The Spanish-American War, 1898   Birth of Aviation in the United States, 1903

NEG. NO. 24823

305

LANDING OF COLUMBUS, 1492

AMERICA IN HISTORY

PIZARRO'S CONQUEST OF PERU, 1533

ENTRY OF CORTEZ INTO THE HALLS OF MONTEZUMA, 1521

MIDNIGHT BURIAL OF DE SOTO IN THE MISSISSIPPI, 1542

POCAHONTAS SAVING LIFE OF CAPT. JOHN SMITH, 1607

LANDING OF PILGRIMS AT PLYMOUTH, MASS., 1620

307

COLONIZATION OF NEW ENGLAND

PENN'S TREATY WITH THE INDIANS, 1682

BATTLE OF LEXINGTON, 1775

PEACE BETWEEN GOVERNOR OGLETHORPE AND THE INDIANS, 1732

READING OF THE DECLARATION OF INDEPENDENCE, 1776   SURRENDER OF CORNWALLIS AT YORKTOWN, 1781

DEATH OF TECUMSEH AT THE BATTLE OF THAMES, 1813

ENTRY OF GENERAL SCOTT INTO THE CITY OF MEXICO, 1847

NEG. NO. 572

DISCOVERY OF GOLD IN CALIFORNIA, 1848

THE SPANISH-AMERICAN WAR, 1898

THE CIVIL WAR, 1865

BIRTH OF AVIATION IN THE UNITED STATES, 1903

HOUSE WING

Cornwallis Sues for Cessation of Hostilities Under the Flag of Truce was painted by Constantino Brumidi in 1857. Painted originally on the south wall of the House Chamber, this fresco was covered when the chamber was remodeled in 1950. Its historic beauty was again made visible when it was moved in 1961 to its present location and restored by Allyn Cox. The strap of the briefcase lower right, is signed "C. Brumidi Artist, Citizen of the U.S."

The scene is the headquarters of General Washington at Yorktown on October 17, 1781. Washington is standing, in the act of receiving the letter from the emissary sent by Lord Cornwallis under the flag of truce. The British general requested a 24 hour cessation of hostilities while the terms of surrender might be considered, but Washington, fearing the arrival of the British fleet, gave only a 2 hour cease-fire order. Cornwallis was thus forced into the final surrender which occurred on October 19, 1781. Lord Cornwallis was not present at either of these historic events.

NEG. NO. 22180

Cornwallis Sues for Cessation of Hostilities Under the Flag of Truce
Constantino Brumidi, 1857, 7′ 11½″ x 10′ 10″
Members' Private Dining Room, H–117

House Committee on Appropriations, H–143

The four lunettes in this room were designed for the Committee on Insular Affairs which met here when Henry Lyman Sayen was commissioned in 1903 to provide suitable paintings. The four scenes are oil on canvas and were in place by 1905.

Rule of Justice, north wall

In distinct contrast to the lunette opposite, the center figure represents justice. Commerce, industry and agriculture are depicted symbolically as flourishing. No illustration.

Rule of Tyranny, south wall

The central figure symbolizes tyranny. Represented as powerless under her stifling control are figures representing industry, labor, agriculture, trade and commerce. A veiled figure in the distance symbolizes change. No illustration.

NEG. NO. 26683

Good Government, west wall

The peaceful conditions of the insular possessions under the administration of the United States are portrayed. The central figure is that of a woman carrying a vessel on her shoulder while women on either side pursue domestic activities.

NEG. NO. 26682

Primitive Agriculture, east wall

Prior to its installation in 1905, this mural was exhibited in the Pennsylvania Academy of Fine Arts during the Centenary Exhibit. The primitive method of agriculture is depicted.

The decorations in this room are by Constantino Brumidi and were the first fresco decorations in the United States Capitol. They were painted in 1855–56 when this room was occupied by the Agriculture Committee. The two murals and the portrayals of the four seasons are in fresco. The wall scenes and medallion heads are in oil.

NEG. NO. 26671

CALLING OF CINCINNATUS FROM THE PLOW, east wall

Early Roman hero of the 4th century B.C. is portrayed as he left his own small farm to save Rome.

NEG. NO. 26670

CALLING OF PUTNAM FROM THE PLOW TO THE REVOLUTION, west wall

Israel Putnam of Massachusetts, one of the heroes of the American Revolution, left his plow in the furrow and hastened to Cambridge and the battle of Breed's Hill, June 16, 1775.

314

NEG. NO. 26668

HARVESTING GRAIN WITH A McCORMICK REAPER
H–144, north wall.

NEG. NO. 26669

CUTTING GRAIN WITH A SICKLE
H–144, south wall.

AUTUMN   NEG. NO. 26666

WINTER   NEG. NO. 26667

FOUR SEASONS
Constantino Brumidi
H–144

316

SPRING   NEG. NO. 26664

SUMMER   NEG. NO. 26665

317

House Corridors

The decorations on the ceilings and walls of the east corridor, first floor, in the House wing were executed by Allyn Cox to complement the Brumidi frescoes on the Senate side of the Capitol. Research and preliminary drawings began in 1971, the actual painting started in February 1973, and the work was completed July 22, 1974. Mr. Cox was assisted by Cliff Young and John Roach.

The work, a gift of the U.S. Capitol Historical Society, was authorized by H. J. Res. 169, 92nd Congress.

Meeting Places of Congress

Albany, N.Y., Old Stadt Huys, 1754	NEG. NO. 38845
New York City, N.Y., Old City Hall, 1765	NEG. NO. 38846
Philadelphia, Pa., Carpenters' Hall, 1774	NEG. NO. 38847
Philadelphia, Pa., Independence Hall, 1775	NEG. NO. 38848
Baltimore, Md., Old Congress Hall, 1776	NEG. NO. 38849
York, Pa., Old Court House, 1777	NEG. NO. 38850
Princeton, N.J., Nassau Hall, 1783	NEG. NO. 38851
Annapolis, Md., State House, 1783	NEG. NO. 38852
Trenton, N.J., French Arms Tavern, 1784	NEG. NO. 38853
New York City, N.Y., Federal Hall, 1785	NEG. NO. 38854
Philadelphia, Pa., Congress Hall, 1790	NEG. NO. 38855
Washington, D.C., U.S. Capitol, 1800	NEG. NO. 38856
Washington, D.C., Blodgett's Hotel, 1814	NEG. NO. 38857
Washington, D.C., Brick Capitol, 1815	NEG. NO. 38858
Washington, D.C., U.S. Capitol, 1829	NEG. NO. 38859
Washington, D.C., U.S. Capitol, 1867	NEG. NO. 38860

Scenes of Historic Events

Washington and L'Enfant exploring the site of the Capitol, 1791	NEG. NO. 38839
Jefferson presents the competition for the design of a Capitol to the District Commissioners (Johnson, Stuart and Carroll), 1792	NEG. NO. 38861
Washington laying the cornerstone of the Capitol, 1793	NEG. NO. 38838
Burning of the Capitol by the British, 1814	NEG. NO. 38843
First Inauguration (Jackson's) on the steps of the Capitol, 1829	NEG. NO. 38837
Old House Chamber, 1838	NEG. NO. 38841
Rotunda as a hospital, Civil War, 1862	NEG. NO. 38842
Lincoln ordering the building of the dome to continue during the war, 1863	NEG. NO. 38840
Outer lobby of the House during the passage of the Civil Rights Bill, 1866	NEG. NO. 38844

Portraits of Architects of the Capitol

William Thornton	NEG. NO. 38861
Benjamin H. Latrobe	ALL ON NEG. NO. 39547
Charles Bulfinch	
Thomas U. Walter	
Edward Clark	
Elliott Woods	ALL ON NEG. NO. 39548
David Lynn	
J. George Stewart	
George M. White	

Portraits of Artists and Planners

Constantino Brumidi	NEG. NO. 38862
John Trumbull	ALL ON NEG. NO. 39549
Pierre Charles L'Enfant	
Thomas Crawford	
Frederick Law Olmsted	

Sculpture Depicted in the Lunettes

Justice	NEG. NO. 38868
Tripoli Monument	NEG. NO. 38869
George Washington	NEG. NO. 38870
Woodsman	NEG. NO. 38867

Inscriptions

You Are The Rulers And The Ruled—Adlai Stevenson

One Country One Constitution One Destiny—Daniel Webster

Liberty And Union One And Inseparable—Daniel Webster

Here Sir The People Govern—Alexander Hamilton

This Government/The Offspring Of Our Own Choice/Uninfluenced And Unawed/Has A Just Claim To Your Confidence And Support—George Washington

Man Is Not Made For The State/But The State For Man/And It Derives Its Just Powers/Only From The Consent Of The Governed—Thomas Jefferson

We Have Built No Temple/But The Capitol/We Consult No Common Oracle/But The Constitution—Rufus Choate

BURNING OF THE CAPITOL BY THE BRITISH, 1814
ROTUNDA AS A HOSPITAL DURING THE CIVIL WAR, 1862
Allyn Cox, 1974
Corridor, House wing, first floor

319

MEETING PLACES OF CONGRESS
Blodgett's Hotel, 1814, Old Brick Capitol, 1815, U.S. Capitol, 1829, and U.S. Capitol, 1867
Allyn Cox, 1974
Corridor, House wing, first floor

SENATE WING

DEMOCRATIC POLICY COMMITTEE ROOM, S–118

Originally, this room was occupied by the Senate Foreign Relations Committee. About 1874 Constantino Brumidi painted the profiles of the early chairmen of that committee on the walls. Later, an unidentified artist added four eagles in distemper to the ceiling decorations.

NEG. NO. 26992

EAGLE
S–118

NEG. NO. 26999

WILLIAM S. ALLEN, 1845–1846
S–118, south wall

NEG. NO. 26997

HENRY CLAY, 1834–1836
S–118, north wall

NEG. NO. 26998

SIMON E. CAMERON, 1871–1877
S–118, east wall

NEG. NO. 26996

CHARLES W. SUMNER, 1861–1871
S–118, west wall

321

SENATE APPROPRIATIONS COMMITTEE ROOMS,
S–127, S–128 AND S–129

The decorations in the Senate Appropriations
Committee rooms, S–127, S–128 and S–129,
were designed between 1858 and 1871 for the
committees which originally used the rooms. The
allegorical groupings in S–127 were designed for
the Committee on Naval Affairs, those in S–128
and S–129 for the Military Affairs Committee.

S–127   No Illustrations
DECORATIONS BY CONSTANTINO BRUMIDI

> Ancient Porticoes and Antique Vessels
> Indian Heads
> Maidens of the Navy
> Marine Gods and Goddesses

S–128
DECORATIONS BY CONSTANTINO BRUMIDI

> Boston Massacre, 1770
> Battle of Lexington, 1775
> Death of General Wooster, 1777
> Washington at Valley Forge, 1778
> Storming of Stony Point, 1779

Panel and pilaster designs were by Brumidi,
and painted by James Leslie. A medallion head
of Liberty, surrounded by flags and weapons of
war is on the west wall. The ceiling is frescoed
with victors' wreaths, shields and other emblems.

S–129   No Illustrations
DECORATIONS BY CARL RAKEMAN, 1909

Generals of the American Revolution

> Horatio Gates (north wall)
> Joseph Warren (south wall)
> George Washington (east wall)
> Anthony Wayne (west wall)

NEG. NO. 26220

WALL PANEL
Representing ancient and modern arms and
   armor of different nations
Designed by Constantino Brumidi; painted
   by James Leslie, 89″ x 20″
S–128

BATTLE OF LEXINGTON, 1775
Constantino Brumidi
S–128, south wall

BOSTON MASSACRE, 1770
Constantino Brumidi, 1871
S–128, north wall

DEATH OF GENERAL WOOSTER, 1777
Constantino Brumidi
S–128, north wall

STORMING OF STONY POINT, 1779
Constantino Brumidi, 1871
S–128, east wall

WASHINGTON AT VALLEY FORGE, 1778
Constantino Brumidi, 1871
S–128, south wall

LYNDON B. JOHNSON ROOM, S–211

Constantino Brumidi originally decorated this room for the Senate Library, 1858–1867. There are no illustrations. The ceiling murals represent:

Geography
History
Physics
Telegraph
Three Graces (4 groups)

OFFICE OF THE VICE PRESIDENT, S–212

In 1876 when S–212 was used by the Sergeant at Arms, Constantino Brumidi painted allegorical designs on the ceiling. There are no illustrations.

Columbia Welcoming the South back into the Union, signed Brumidi 1876
Implements of War Destroyed
Rods United—"E Pluribus Unum"
Secession and Products of North and South
War and Strife

SENATE RECEPTION ROOM, S–213

Allegorical groups in the ceiling were painted by Constantino Brumidi 1871–2. They are not illustrated.

CIRCULAR ARCH, south

La Jurisprudence (Jurisprudence), southeast
La Force (Strength or Power), northwest
La Sapience (Wisdom), northeast
La Prudence (Discretion), southwest

GROINED ARCH, north

La Guerre (War), west
La Paix (Peace), east
Les Sciences (Sciences), north
Les Arts de l'Industrie (Industrial Arts), south

A painting depicting George Washington in Consultation with Thomas Jefferson and Alexander Hamilton is on the south wall. Portraits of five Senators were added in 1959. See page 34.

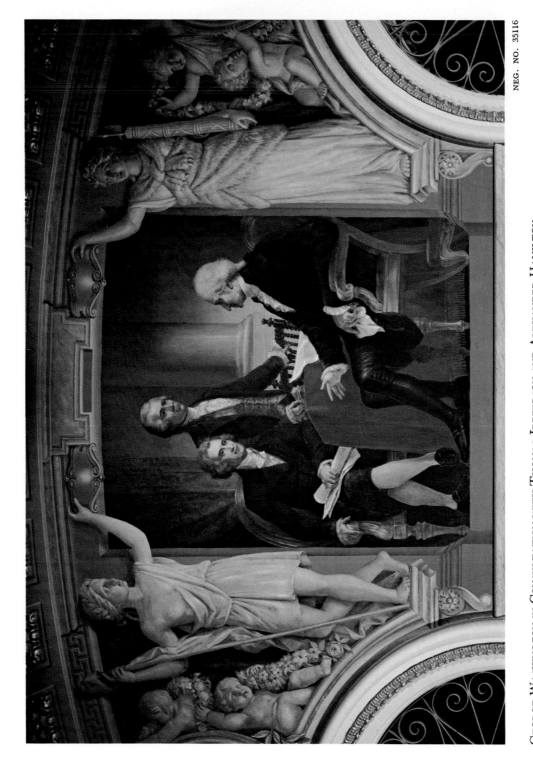

George Washington in Consultation with Thomas Jefferson and Alexander Hamilton
Constantino Brumidi, 1870–73
S–213

Constantino Brumidi began his oil and fresco work in this room about 1859. For many years the Presidents used this room as the ceremonial chamber for signing documents. The portraits of the five members of George Washington's first cabinet and symbolic paintings completely cover the walls and ceilings.

There are no illustrations for the symbolic Madonna figures in the ceiling representing Religion, Legislation, Liberty and Executive Authority.

NEG. NO. 35103

GEORGE WASHINGTON
Constantino Brumidi
S–216

Thomas Jefferson, Secretary of State
Constantino Brumidi
S–216

328

ALEXANDER HAMILTON, Secretary of the Treasury
Constantino Brumidi
S–216

HENRY KNOX, Secretary of War
Constantino Brumidi
S–216

EDMUND RANDOLPH, Attorney General
Constantino Brumidi
S–216

SAMUEL OSGOOD, Postmaster General
Constantino Brumidi
S–216

332

BREWSTER

WILLIAM BREWSTER—Religion
S–216, ceiling

CHRISTOPHER COLUMBUS—Discovery
S–216, ceiling

Benjamin Franklin—History
S–216, ceiling

Americus Vespucius—Exploration
S–216, ceiling

336

SENATE CORRIDORS

The first floor corridors of the Senate wing are lined with mural monochrome medallion portraits and decorative subjects by Constantino Brumidi. They are not illustrated. Negative numbers for black and white prints are included for those works that have been photographed. Each portrait medallion measures approximately 18″ in diameter exclusive of the decorative border.

MAIN CORRIDOR

Adams (unidentified)	
Henry Clay	NEG. NO. 24261
Andrew Jackson	NEG. NO. 23678
Daniel Webster	
Chancellor Kent	
Justice Joseph Story	
Robert R. Livingston, 1878	
14 oval landscapes in oil	
(walls and ceiling), artists are not known	

NORTH CORRIDOR

Silas Deane	NEG. NO. 23672
Benjamin Franklin	NEG. NO. 23677
Horatio Gates	NEG. NO. 23673
Thomas Jefferson	NEG. NO. 23680
Thomas Mifflin	NEG. NO. 23682
Richard Montgomery	NEG. NO. 23683

Daniel Morgan	NEG. NO. 23684
Israel Putnam	NEG. NO. 23674
Jonathan Trumbull	NEG. NO. 23688
Joseph Warren	NEG. NO. 23689

Cession of Louisiana, lunette

Signing of First Treaty of Peace with Great Britain, 1782, lunette, 1874, after a sketch by Benjamin West

SOUTH CORRIDOR
8 studies in oil (animals)
8 ovals in oil (U.S. Shields)

WEST CORRIDOR

Charles Carroll	NEG. NO. 23671
John Hancock	NEG. NO. 23675
Francis Hopkinson	NEG. NO. 23676
John Jay	NEG. NO. 23679
Robert R. Livingston	NEG. NO. 23681
Robert Morris	NEG. NO. 23685
Roger Sherman	NEG. NO. 23686
Charles Thomson	NEG. NO. 23687

Authority Consults the Written Law, mural
Columbus and the Indian Maiden, mural
Bartolome de Las Casas, the Apostle of the Indians, lunette
Bellona, the Roman Goddess of War, lunette, 1875

NEG. NO. 35105

CESSION OF LOUISIANA
(Negotiations for the acquisition of Louisiana)
Constantino Brumidi, 1875
Senate wing, first floor, north corridor

337

Authority Consults the Written Law
Constantino Brumidi
Senate wing, first floor, west corridor

Columbus and the Indian Maiden
Constantino Brumidi
Senate wing, first floor, west corridor

338

PATENT CORRIDOR

Constantino Brumidi determined the theme of his decorations here in 1873 from the committees occupying the rooms off this first floor corridor. The Committee on Patents occupied the larger room and the lunettes and ceiling decorations depicting important inventions attest to this influence.

A lunette of Benjamin Franklin in his laboratory is above the door of the room originally used by the Committee on Post Offices and Post Roads.

John Fitch, working on his model of a steamboat, is not illustrated.

The Robert Fulton lunette is the largest and Brumidi has included his steamboat, the *Clermont*, and the New Jersey Palisades in the background. His benefactor, De Witt Clinton, is shown in a portrait on a nearby easel.

NEG. NO. 36384

ROBERT FULTON
Constantino Brumidi
Patent corridor

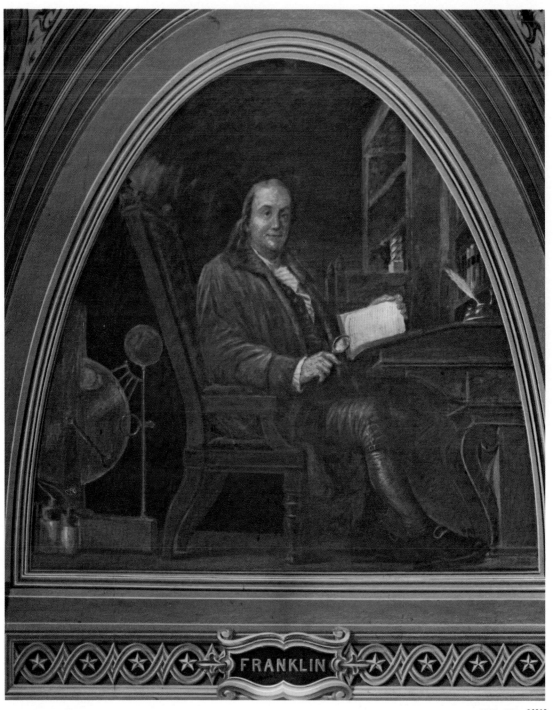

BENJAMIN FRANKLIN
Constantino Brumidi
Patent corridor

Exterior Sculpture

Bronze Doors
Fountain
Statues
Tympanums

ROTUNDA BRONZE DOORS

The bronze doors at the eastern entrance to the Rotunda depicting events in the life of Christopher Columbus were designed and modeled by Randolph Rogers in Rome, Italy in 1858. They were cast in 1861 in Munich, Germany by Ferdinand von Miller at the Royal Bavarian Foundry.

In November 1863 the doors were installed between Statuary Hall and the House extension. Because of their massiveness and great beauty, it was felt they were worthy of a focal location, and in 1871 they were moved to the Rotunda entrance. In 1961 the doors were moved 32 feet east when the East Front of the Capitol was extended.

The doors, also called the Rogers Doors, have two valves with four panels in each valve, surmounted by a semicircular tympanum.

TYMPANUM

The Landing of Columbus in the New World at Guanahani, Watling Island, called San Salvador by Columbus, October 12, 1492.

LEFT VALVE

Departure of Columbus From Palos. Columbus is confiding his son to the monks before he embarks upon his first voyage, August 3, 1492. His ships lie waiting in the harbor.

Audience at the Court of Ferdinand and Isabella. Queen Isabella is seated in state, leaning forward and seemingly deeply interested in what Columbus is saying. King Ferdinand is by her side. On April 17, 1492 the agreement between Columbus and their Majesties was signed.

Columbus' Departure From the Convent of La Rabida, near Palos, to visit the Spanish Court, 1492. It was to this convent he had come with his small son Diego, weary, penniless and discouraged. He was befriended by Juan Perez,

prior of the convent and Confessor to Queen Isabella, and by Lady Bobadilla, an attendant of Isabella, who urged the Queen to assist Columbus in his expedition.

Columbus Before the Council of Salamanca is unfolding his grand theory—a new route to the East. In 1487, after long delays, the Council declared the project vain and impossible.

RIGHT VALVE

Columbus' First Encounter With the Indians. One of the sailors is seen carrying an Indian girl prisoner on his shoulders. This action aroused the stern indignation of Columbus.

Entry of Columbus Into Barcelona. Waving banners welcome Columbus to the Spanish Court as he returns from his first voyage in 1493.

Columbus in Chains. Don Francisco de Bobadilla, sent out by the Court to investigate charges preferred against Columbus, had him placed in chains and returned to Spain, November 1500. On board the vessel, the officers wished to relieve him of his chains, but Columbus replied with deep feeling, "I will wear them as a memento of the gratitude of princes."

Columbus was cleared of the charges, and in 1502 set sail once more for the New World.

Death of Columbus. The last rites of the Catholic Church have been administered. Friends and attendants are around him and a priest holds up a crucifix for him to kiss. Columbus returned from his last voyage poor, sick and disconsolate. He sought redress at the Spanish Court, and although he had been cleared of all the charges against him, he failed in his attempt. With the death of Queen Isabella in 1504, Columbus had lost his influence at the Court.

Columbus died at Valladolid, the 20th of May, 1506.

In niches on the sides of the doors and between the panels are sixteen small statues of contemporaries of Columbus. They are identified on the diagram.

Vespucci, the much trusted friend of Columbus.

Ojeda, an early Spanish adventurer to the New World who lacked fealty to Columbus.

Cortez, conqueror of Mexico.

Perez, prior of the Convent of La Rabida and firm friend of Columbus.

Standing in pairs on the inside borders are:

Mendoza, Archbishop of Toledo and Grand Cardinal of Spain who had great influence at court.

Alexander VI, Roman Pontiff.

Isabella and *Ferdinand*, Spanish Monarchs.

Lady Beatrix de Bobadilla, marchioness of Moya and early friend of Columbus.

Charles VIII, King of France.

Henry VII of England, a patron of navigation who regarded with favor the theory of Columbus.

John II, King of Portugal who reigned during the period of Columbus' first two voyages.

At the top of the last row four additional explorers complete the design.

Pizarro, conqueror of Peru.

Balboa, Spanish discoverer and adventurer.

B. Columbus, brother of Christopher, appointed by him lieutenant governor of the Indies.

Pinzon, commander of the *Pinta* who first saw land, September 25, 1492.

OTHER DECORATIONS

Between the panels and at the top and bottom of the doors are 10 small sculptured heads. They are representative of the historians who have written of Columbus' voyages from his own time to the mid-nineteenth century.

Above the tympanum can be seen the bust of Christopher Columbus, the American Eagle and draped flags. The frame of the door is covered with heraldic emblems. On the extreme edges of the doors are four draped figures representing the continents of Asia, Europe, Africa and America.

ROTUNDA DOORS
Randolph Rogers, bronze, 16'8'' x 9'9''
East Rotunda entrance

345

HOUSE BRONZE DOORS

The bronze doors at the east portico entrance, House wing, were designed by Thomas Crawford in Rome, Italy in 1855–57. Upon his death William H. Rinehart executed the models from the Crawford sketches, 1863–67.

The models were shipped from Leghorn, Italy in 1867, but remained stored in the Crypt of the Capitol until 1903 when they were cast by Melzar H. Mosman of Chicopee, Massachusetts. The doors were installed in 1905.

The bronze doors of the House wing are comparable to the Senate doors. Each valve consists of three panels and a medallion depicting great events in American history.

LEFT VALVE

Wyoming Massacre, Pennsylvania. During the Revolution a large proportion of the men of Wyoming Valley, Pennsylvania joined the Continental Army. A number of Loyalists remained there, and in 1778 they were joined by the British troops and their Indian allies. The settlers who had taken refuge in Forty Fort, near Wilkes-Barre, were outnumbered 1100 to 400. July 3, 1778 after a desperate battle, the settlers were forced to capitulate. The massacre followed.

Battle of Lexington. General Gage, the British Commander in Boston, heard that the Colonists were collecting arms and ammunition. He determined to prevent rebellion by seizing these supplies. The colonists were warned and during the night of April 18, 1775, Paul Revere and William Dawes rode to warn the Minutemen. The British troops were marching toward Concord and met the small Militia. Here on April 19, 1775 occurred the famous "shot heard 'round the World"—the beginning of the Revolutionary War.

Presentation of Flag and Medal to General Nathanael Greene. In 1778 Great Britain shifted the attack upon the colonies to the South. Nathanael Greene replaced General Gates as Commander in the South and with the help of loyal American frontiersmen, the British camps were raided. This panel depicts General Greene receiving a medal and flag after the Battle of Eutaw Springs on September 8, 1781 for expelling the British from South Carolina.

Medallion—Death of General Montgomery. Late in 1775, Congress sent a two column military expedition to Canada, one under Richard Montgomery via New York, and the other under Benedict Arnold via Maine, hoping to arouse the French Canadians to revolt against the British. The expedition failed. In the attack on Quebec, December 31, 1775, General Montgomery was killed.

RIGHT VALVE

Public Reading of the Declaration of Independence at Philadelphia. On July 4, 1776 the Second Continental Congress adopted the Declaration of Independence. The first public reading was July 8, 1776, when the Declaration of Independence was officially proclaimed in Philadelphia.

The Signing of the Treaty at Paris Between the United States and Great Britain. The Revolution ended in October 1781, but it was not until September 3, 1783 that the Treaty of Paris was signed. The panel depicts the negotiations between the United States commissioners and the British representatives. The liberal concessions to the United States were largely due to the efforts of Benjamin Franklin.

Washington's Farewell to His Officers in New York. After the Treaty of Peace was signed Washington was leaving New York for Philadelphia. His officers of the war years gathered at Fraunces Tavern, December 4, 1783, to say good-bye. When he entered the room he could scarcely command his voice. He spoke briefly, and they drank a toast. Washington requested each man to come forward and take his hand. General Knox, who stood nearest, was first to clasp his hand. The panel depicts this touching farewell.

Medallion—Benjamin Franklin in His Studio. Benjamin Franklin, an inventor, a signer of the Declaration of Independence and the Constitution; a Member of the Continental Congress and Minister to France 1776–1785, is shown in his studio studying electricity.

DECORATIVE PANEL	DECORATIVE PANEL
MASSACRE OF WYOMING, PA. JULY 3, 1778	PUBLIC READING OF THE DECLARATION OF INDEPENDENCE AT PHILADELPHIA
BATTLE OF LEXINGTON APRIL 19, 1775	TREATY OF PEACE AT PARIS BETWEEN U.S. AND GREAT BRITAIN SEPTEMBER 3, 1783
PRESENTATION OF THE FLAG AND MEDAL TO GENERAL NATHANAEL GREENE	WASHINGTON'S FAREWELL TO HIS OFFICERS-NEW YORK DECEMBER 4, 1783
DEATH OF GENERAL MONTGOMERY DECEMBER 31, 1775	BENJAMIN FRANKLIN IN HIS STUDIO

O. I. P.

House Doors
Designed by Thomas Crawford, bronze
Executed by William H. Rinehart, 14′7″ x 7′4″
East House portico entrance

SENATE BRONZE DOORS

The Senate bronze doors were designed and modeled by Thomas Crawford in Rome, Italy, between 1855–57. After his death in 1857, William H. Rinehart was commissioned to complete the work and the models were shipped to America in 1864. They were cast by James T. Ames at his foundry in Chicopee, Massachusetts 1864–68, and placed late in 1868.

Each valve consists of three panels and a medallion depicting events in the life of George Washington and Revolutionary War scenes.

LEFT VALVE

Laying of the Cornerstone of the United States Capitol. On September 18, 1793, the cornerstone of the United States Capitol was laid in the southeast corner of the north wing, with Masonic rites. President George Washington, with the trowel in his right hand, is laying the cornerstone.

Inauguration of George Washington as First President. The inauguration took place April 30, 1789 on the balcony of Federal Hall in New York City. Chancellor Livingston is administering the oath of office, and George Washington's right hand is resting upon the open Bible. John Adams, Vice President, is shown on the right, with other noted guests at the left of the panel.

Ovation for George Washington at Trenton, New Jersey. The panel depicts George Washington receiving an ovation at Trenton, New Jersey en route to his 1789 inaugural in New York. A triumphal arch of flowers was built over the bridge at Assumpink Creek, the place where Washington had defeated the British. Small girls strewed flowers before him as he slowly rode across the bridge, accompanied by the singing of the multitudes gathered to honor him.

Allegorical Medallion of Peace and Agriculture. In this tranquil scene are figures representing Infancy, Maternity, Childhood, Youth and Manhood. The figures surround a plow which contains a sheaf of wheat, the symbol of fertility. The Youth holds a book in his hand.

RIGHT VALVE

Battle of Bunker Hill and the Death of General Warren. On June 16, 1775, the British Army intended to seize and fortify Bunker Hill, opposite the city of Boston. Colonel Prescott, with a thousand American patriots, entrenched on Breed's Hill, lower, but nearer Boston. Re-enforcements led by Colonel Prescott and General Warren came to his aid in the intense hand-to-hand battle. General Warren was shot and in this panel Colonel Prescott is shown supporting the dying General.

Battle of Monmouth and the Rebuke of General Lee. On June 18, 1778, the British Army evacuated Philadelphia and proceeded through New Jersey toward New York. General Charles Lee and General Lafayette were in command of the Militia that was to harass the rear of the British Army in order to bring on a general engagement. A successful attack was made, but Lee failed to hold the ground. General Washington met the retreating troops, and rallied them. The panel depicts General Washington rebuking General Lee with great severity for his failure to obey his orders.

Battle of Yorktown and the Gallantry of Alexander Hamilton. The scene is at the close of the war when Cornwallis was entrenched at Yorktown, Virginia. Hamilton was granted permission by General Washington to lead the attack on one of the two redoubts that had to be taken. The center figure of this panel is Alexander Hamilton, gallantly leading the attack.

Allegorical Medallion of War. A Hessian soldier is in a death struggle with the farmer, who is protecting his wife and child from the soldier's assault.

NEG. NO. 22712

O.I.P.

Senate Doors
Designed by Thomas Crawford, bronze
Executed by William H. Rinehart,
   14′ 5½″ x 7′ 4″
East Senate portico entrance

AMATEIS BRONZE DOORS

The Amateis bronze doors were designed and cast for the main central entrance of the West Front. They were completed in 1910, but they could not be placed because the enabling legislation for the improvement of the West Front was not enacted. The doors were exhibited at the Corcoran Gallery of Art for four years. In 1914 they were loaned to the Smithsonian Institution where they were on exhibition in the Natural History Building until 1967. At that time they were returned to the Capitol and in 1972 they were placed on display.

The doors consist of eight panels and a transom depicting allegorical and symbolic accomplishments of America.

There are twenty-eight medallions and eighteen statuettes bordering the eight panels and the transom.

Transom

Apotheosis of America. America, in a chariot drawn by Lions, is symbolic of Strength. The Lions are led by a Child, signifying the superiority of the Intellect over Brute Force. At the sides of the chariot are allegorical figures of Education, Architecture, Painting, Literature, Music, Sculpture, Commerce, Mining and Industry. Statuettes of Benjamin Franklin and Thomas Jefferson stand on either side in the border of the panel. Medallions in the four corners are Horace Mann, educator, George Peabody, financier of educational institutions, Johns Hopkins, philanthropist, and Ralph Waldo Emerson, philosopher.

Left Valve

Jurisprudence is represented by the Supreme Court presided over by Chief Justice John Marshall. A bust of George Washington is shown above the chair of the Chief Justice. Statuettes on the left and right are of Daniel Webster and James Madison. Above are medallions of Patrick Henry, patriot, Rufus Choate, lawyer, and Chief Justice Roger B. Taney.

Sciences. Scientific workers from Hipparchus, Greek astronomer, to Charles R. Darwin. At the sides are statuettes of Oliver W. Gibbs, chemist, and Joseph Henry, physicist. The medallions portray James D. Dana, geologist, Simon Newcomb, astronomer, Alexander Graham Bell, inventor of the telephone, and Samuel F. B. Morse, inventor of the telegraph.

Fine Arts. Figures of Virgil, Dante, Shakespeare, Goethe, Hugo, Palestrina, Beethoven, Rossini and Homer. Above them is a flying figure of Genius. The statuettes at the sides are of Edgar Allen Poe, writer, and William Thornton, first Architect of the U.S. Capitol. The medallions portray Gilbert Stuart, painter, and Henry Kirke Brown, sculptor.

Mining. Scene at a mine. On each side of this panel are statuettes of James W. Marshall, discoverer of gold in California, and Alexander L. Holley, mining engineer. The medallions portray E. B. Case, engineer, Clarence King, geologist, and Abram Hewitt, industrialist.

Right Valve

Agriculture. A typical harvest scene. The statuettes are of Samuel G. Morton, physician and ethnologist, and James Wilson, agriculturist. The medallions portray John Pitkin Norton, agricultural chemist, Senator Justin S. Morrill, and Benjamin Bussey, agricultural chemist.

Iron and Electricity. Iron and electric workers. The statuettes are of Peter Cooper, philanthropist, and Henry A. Rowland, physicist. Medallions show Matthias W. Baldwin, founder of the locomotive works and Thomas Alva Edison, inventor.

Engineering. Workers laying a railroad track. A bridge is in the background. Statuettes show James B. Eads, builder of the St. Louis bridge, and Thomas L. Casey, engineer. Medallions portray Washington A. Roebling, builder of the Brooklyn bridge, and Stevens, builder of the transcontinental railroads.

Naval Architecture and Commerce is represented by a figure typifying Architecture, showing Commerce, Industry and Agriculture the places on a globe where they can dispose of their wares. The globe is held by a Youth. A sailor is holding a flag surmounted by a liberty cap, significant of an open door policy. Statuettes portray Robert Fulton, inventor of the steamboat, and John Ericsson, designer of the *Monitor*. Medallions depict Eli Whitney, inventor of the cotton gin, Elias Howe, inventor of the sewing machine, John C. Fremont, the "Pathfinder," Cyrus W. Field, financier of the Atlantic Cable, and John Lenthall, naval constructor.

NEG. NO. 36090

O. I. P.

AMATEIS DOORS
Signed l.l. L. Amateis, Sculptor, Washington,
   D.C., 1910; bronze, 13' 10'' x 7' 8½''
Center building, first floor

BARTHOLDI FOUNTAIN

Designed by the same sculptor who created the Statue of Liberty, this fountain was sent by the French government for the 1876 Centennial Exposition in Philadelphia. It was purchased by the Committee on Public Buildings and Grounds and moved to the Botanic Garden, then on the mall. When the Garden was relocated in 1932, the fountain was also moved to its present location.

Illuminated originally with gas, it is intended to embody an allegorical representation of the elements of *Water* and *Light*.

It is 30' high, weighs 40 tons, basin 26' in diameter, statue 11'.

NEG. NO. 34060

BARTHOLDI FOUNTAIN
Frederic Auguste Bartholdi, iron bronzed
Purchased 1877
Botanic Garden

DISCOVERY AND RESCUE

Originally located on the south cheek block, east central front steps, the grouping became so badly deteriorated that in 1958 when the Extension of the East Front began, "Discovery" was crated and placed in storage. Overall dimensions are 15'11½" high, 8'4½" wide and 6'½" deep.

As a companion piece to "Discovery," "Rescue" was placed on the north cheek block, east central front steps. It, too, was removed and placed in storage when the Extension of the East Front began. Overall dimensions are 11'9" high, 10'2" wide and 7'3" deep.

NEG. NO. 100

NEG. NO. 102

DISCOVERY OF AMERICA
Luigi Persico, marble
Erected 1844
Purchased by Stats. L., vol. 5, p. 173
Transferred to Smithsonian Institution 1976

RESCUE
Horatio Greenough, marble
Erected 1853
Purchased by Congress, March 3, 1837
Transferred to Smithsonian Institution 1976

STATUE OF FREEDOM

Surmounting the Dome of the Capitol and facing east is the bronze Statue of Freedom. It was designed by Thomas Crawford in Rome, Italy, in 1856. The plaster model was received in 1858 and the casting was done in the shops of another sculptor, Clark Mills, in northeast Washington, D.C.

The figure is that of a woman clad in flowing draperies. Her right hand rests upon the hilt of a sheathed sword, and her left holds a wreath and shield. At her waist a brooch composed of the letters "U.S." holds her robes in place. The head is covered by a helmet encircled with stars and topped with a bold arrangement of feathers and an eagle's head.

Freedom is 19'6" high, weighs 14,985 pounds and cost $23,796.82. Its placement was completed December 2, 1863.

From 1890 to 1967 the plaster model of the Statue of Freedom was on exhibition in the Smithsonian Institution. It is now in storage.

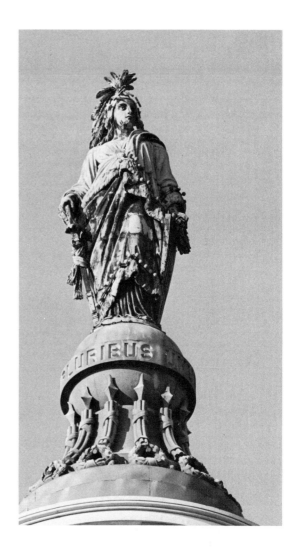

NEG. NO. 27751

STATUE OF FREEDOM
Thomas Crawford, bronze, 19'6"
Dome of the United States Capitol

See also frontispiece

JUSTICE AND HISTORY

The two draped figures of Justice and History recline against a globe. Justice is supporting a volume bearing the inscription "Justice, Law, Order," and her right hand rests on a pair of scales. History holds a scroll incised "History, July 1776."

Overall length of the sculpture is 11'2'', length of the reclining figure of History 5'4", length of the reclining figure of Justice 5'10'', height of each figure 3'10'' and the depth of the sculpture is 2'2".

These figures became irreparably disfigured through deterioration and granulation of the marble. Authorization and appropriation to make replicas from casts of the original Justice and History were provided for by P.L. 93–145, 93rd Congress. Francesco Tonelli of the Vermont Marble Co. was the carver. The reproductions were placed December 1974.

The original figures may be seen in the Capitol terminal of the Senate subway.

NEG. NO. 36281

JUSTICE AND HISTORY
Thomas Crawford, marble
Placed 1863 as part of the Senate wing construction
Above Senate bronze doors, east portico

355

STATUES OF WAR AND PEACE

Luigi Persico executed marble statues of War and Peace in Italy. They arrived at the Capitol in 1834 where they were placed in niches on the East Front portico. Through the years, deterioration of serious proportions affected both statues and in 1958 they were removed when the East Front was extended. The defaced figures were mended so that plaster models could be made from the originals by George Giannetti of Washington, D.C. Carvers were then able to reproduce the new figures in Vermont marble and they were placed in 1960. The 1958 plaster models of War and Peace may be seen in the Cannon House Office Building rotunda, subway level. The original marble figure of War was transferred to the Smithsonian Institution in 1976.

NEG. NO. 20505

NEG. NO. 20504

WAR

Carved in 1958 after the original by Luigi Persico

Niche right of east central entrance

Clad in the costume of a Roman warrior, War stands with a firm, sedate countenance and with no evidence of rage or fury. He assumes the attitude of listening to Peace, who stands on his right.

PEACE

Carved 1958 after the original by Luigi Persico

Niche left of east central entrance

Draped in simple flowing robes, Peace holds in her left hand a fruit-bearing olive branch which she extends toward War. Her attitude is one of sympathy for mankind.

MAJESTY OF LAW

SPIRIT OF JUSTICE

A companion piece to Spirit of Justice, the male figure of the Majesty of Law is portrayed as one who instills reverence for the law and typifies supreme authority and great dignity.

The sheathed sword in his right hand is a symbol of valor. His left hand rests on a book containing the laws of this land with the Seal of the United States on the cover.

The Spirit of Justice is represented by a female figure, likened to Pallas Athene, the great civic goddess who was also wise in the industries of Peace.

In her right hand she holds aloft a lighted lamp symbolizing truth and righteousness. Her left hand around the shoulder of a small boy signifies Temperance with Justice.

NEG. NO. 28642

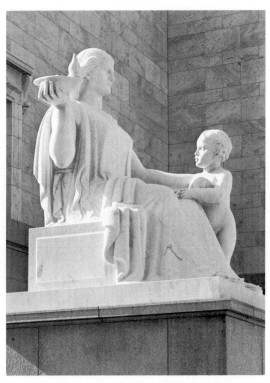

NEG. NO. 28644

MAJESTY OF LAW
C. Paul Jennewein, 1964, marble, approximately
   10'4" x 6'
Rayburn House Office Building, Independence
   Avenue, west pylon

SPIRIT OF JUSTICE
C. Paul Jennewein, 1964, marble, approximately
   10'4" x 6'
Rayburn House Office Building, Independence
   Avenue, east pylon

STATUE OF CHIEF JUSTICE JOHN MARSHALL

The sculptor has given us the posture of Marshall as the great jurist, sitting in the chair he used for so many years, rendering a judicial decision.

On the marble base is incised: "John Marshall, Chief Justice of the United States. Erected by the Bar and the Congress of the United States, A.D. MDCCCLXXXIV." On the north side of the base is a panel in relief, "Minerva Dictating the Constitution to Young America." A companion panel on the south side, "Victory Leading Young America to Swear Fidelity at the Altar of the Union," is depicted in the accompanying photograph.

NEG. NO. 35111

JOHN MARSHALL
William Wetmore Story, bronze, 6'11''
Signed l. base W. W. Story, Roma, 1883
Capitol Grounds, West Front

RHYTONS

These marble accents occur at each side of the wing motives at the east and west ends of the building. The designer, a member of the architectural firm who designed the building, modeled the rhytons after the ancient Greek drinking horn with a mythical chimera with bended knees.

The Ram's head is representative of Wisdom, Power, Strength of Purpose, Defender of Right. The Horn, or Cornucopia, is the classic symbol of abundance and plenty. The rhytons rest on a calyx of water leaves.

NEG. NO. 33261

RHYTONS (8)
Designed by W. H. Livingston, Sr.
Placed 1964, marble, 12½ tons
Rayburn House Office Building

ROBERT A. TAFT MEMORIAL

The simple strength and quiet dignity of the bell tower memorial is symbolic of the man it represents. The shaft of Tennessee marble houses the 27 extraordinarily matched bells which were cast in the Paccard Bell Foundry in Annecy, France. They strike the hour and chime on the quarter hour. By Congressional resolution they play the Star Spangled Banner at 2 p.m. on the 4th of July. During Christmas week religious carols may be heard, and on Sunday hymns are played at four different times.

The Taft Memorial, authorized by Senate Concurrent Resolution 44, 84th Congress, was constructed with funds received by public subscription. Located on the grounds directly north of the Capitol the tower rises 100′ and is 11′ thick and 32′ wide. It rests on a base 55′ x 45′ and 15′ high. Standing on the base is the 10′ bronze statue of Robert A. Taft, and behind it are incised the words:

> This Memorial to Robert A. Taft, presented by the people to the Congress of the United States, stands as tribute to the honesty, indomitable courage and high principles of free government symbolized by his life.

The memorial was dedicated and accepted by the Congress of the United States April, 14, 1959.

NEG. NO. 20747

ROBERT A. TAFT Memorial, 1959
Designed by Douglas W. Orr, architect
United States Capitol Grounds

NEG. NO. 35112

ROBERT A. TAFT, statue
Wheeler Williams, bronze, 1959, 10′
Base of Taft Memorial

TYMPANUMS

America, the central figure, rests her right arm on a shield inscribed "USA" which is supported by an altar bearing the inscription "July 4, 1776." She points to Justice holding the scales and in whose right hand a scroll is inscribed, "Constitution, 17 September 1787." To America's left is an Eagle and the figure of Hope, who rests her arm on an anchor. This grouping conveys the thought that while we cultivate justice, we may strive for success.

The original sandstone figures were executed by Luigi Persico in 1825–28 after a design suggested by President John Quincy Adams. When the East Front was extended, the badly deteriorated figures were removed and restored so that plaster models could be made. From these models the reproductions were carved in Georgia White marble.

The pediment is 81' 6" in length and the figures are 9' high. The plaster models for the reproductions are located in the rotunda of the Cannon House Office Building, subway level. The original sandstone figures are in storage.

NEG. NO. 20892

GENIUS OF AMERICA
Luigi Persico, sandstone, 1825–28
Bruno Mankowski, marble, 1959–60
East Central Pediment

An allegorical group consisting of two figures "Peace Protecting Genius," fills the center of the pediment. An armed Peace, stands erect, draped in a mantle which almost completely hides her breastplate and coat of mail. Her left arm rests on her buckler, which is supported by the altar at her side. In the background is the olive tree of peace. Her right arm is extended in a gesture of protection over the youthful and winged figure of Genius, who nestles confidently at her feet and holds in his right hand the torch of Immortality. The composition is completed by two other groups, symbolizing and typifying the two great fundamental powers of labor, the two great sources of wealth—Agriculture and Industry. A wave at either end of the sculpture symbolizes the Atlantic and Pacific Oceans.

The figures were modeled in Paris, France and Washington, D.C., 1911–1914; carved in Georgia White marble by the Piccirilli Brothers of New York City, 1914–1916 and unveiled August 2, 1916. Extreme length of pediment 80'; height at center about 12'; length of sculpture about 60'.

The plaster models were given to the United States Government in March 1963 by Mrs. Armistead Peter III, a stepdaughter of the artist. They were placed in the Capitol terminal of the subway leading to the Rayburn House Office Building.

NEG. NO. 34881

APOTHEOSIS OF DEMOCRACY
Paul Wayland Bartlett, marble, 1916
House Pediment, East Front

362

The center figure is America with an eagle at her side and the sun at her back. On her left, representing the early days in America, are a woodsman, hunter, Indian chief, Indian mother and child, and an Indian grave. On her right the progress of civilization is depicted in the figures of the soldier, merchant, two youths, the schoolmaster and child, and the mechanic. Completing this side of the tympanum are sheaves of wheat, symbolic of fertility, and an anchor, symbolic of hope, in contrast to the grave at the opposite end of the sculpture of the tympanum.

The figures were modeled in Rome, Italy in 1854; carved at the Capitol 1855–59 from Lee, Massachusetts marble; erected in 1863. The extreme length of the pediment is 80′; height at center about 12′; and the length of the sculpture is about 60′.

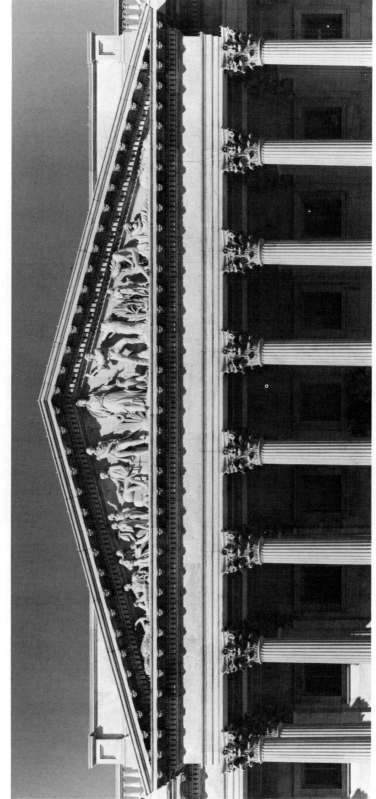

NEG. NO. 34882

PROGRESS OF CIVILIZATION
Thomas Crawford, marble, 1863
Senate Pediment, East Front

RAYBURN HOUSE OFFICE BUILDING

The symbolic American Eagle spreads his wings in the tympanum above the Independence Avenue entrance. The sculpture was part of the Rayburn House Office Building construction.

EAGLE
C. Paul Jennewein, 1964, marble
Rayburn House Office Building

Miscellaneous Works of Art

Sculpture

Vases

Window and Laylights

NEG. NO. 33882

CORINTHIAN CAPITAL, 1825
Crypt

Original column cap and base of sandstone were removed from the East Front when it was extended and duplicated in marble 1958–1961.

NEG. NO. 35107

"CORNCOB" CAPITALS (6), 1809
Designed by Benjamin H. Latrobe; modeled and carved by Giuseppe Franzoni, sandstone
East Front entry, first floor vestibule

NEG. NO. 19914

TOBACCO CAPITALS (16), 1818
Designed by Benjamin H. Latrobe; modeled and carved by Francisco Iardella, sandstone
Lobby of the small rotunda, Senate wing, second floor

The tobacco motiff is also used in the capitals of the 28 columns in the Hall of Columns, House wing, first floor, and were carved about 1855.

366

CAR OF HISTORY (CLOCK)
Carlo Franzoni, marble, 1819
Statuary Hall, north entrance

Clio, the Muse, representing History, stands in the winged car of Time, recording events as they occur. The car rests on a marble globe on which the signs of the zodiac are carved in relief. The chariot wheel is the face of the clock. The works are by Simon Willard.

367

EAGLE

Giuseppe Valaperta, sandstone, 1816

Statuary Hall on the frieze of the entablature below the statue of Liberty

EAGLE

Artist and date unknown, gilt wood, 72″ wing span

S–228, Old Senate Chamber

As early as 1834 there was reference to a gilt eagle in the Old Senate Chamber above the canopy over the chair of the presiding officer. Although specific information is unknown, an eagle has traditionally been in the Chamber.

INDIAN AND THE PIONEER

William H. Rinehart, 1857, bronze, 3′ high

These figures stood on either side of an elaborately carved wooden clock case which was removed and stored after the remodeling of the House Chamber 1940–1951. No illustration.

INDIAN FOUNTAIN
William H. Rinehart, bronze, 1857
SB–14

Acquired by action of the Joint Committee on the Library, 1876, when extensive remodeling no longer left a place for it in the Post Office. The bowl is about 16″ in diameter; the figure is 13″ high.

MASK
Unknown artist, bronze, 1857
SB–14

This mask was over the north entrance to the House Chamber from 1857 to 1950. It was removed when the House Chamber was remodeled in 1950.

PERICLES
Artist and date unknown, bronze, 19½″
H–216, House Appropriations Committee
No records

PHIDIAS
Artist and date unknown, bronze, 19″
H–216, House Appropriations Committee
No records

371

PIONEERS OF THE WEST

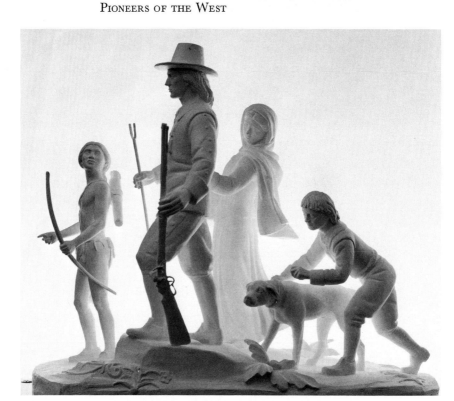

NEG. NO. 37057

SETTLERS OF THE EAST COAST

These groups were made in plaster by Paul Manship in 1965 as suggested statuary for the cheek blocks on the East Central Front when it was extended 1958–1961. They are on display in the Crypt.

SEVRES VASES, 66¾″ high, 25″ diameter
Gifts of the Republic of France, 1918
H–207, Rayburn Room

SEVRES VASES, 68¾″ high, 28″ diameter
Gifts of the Republic of France, 1918
Senate Lobby

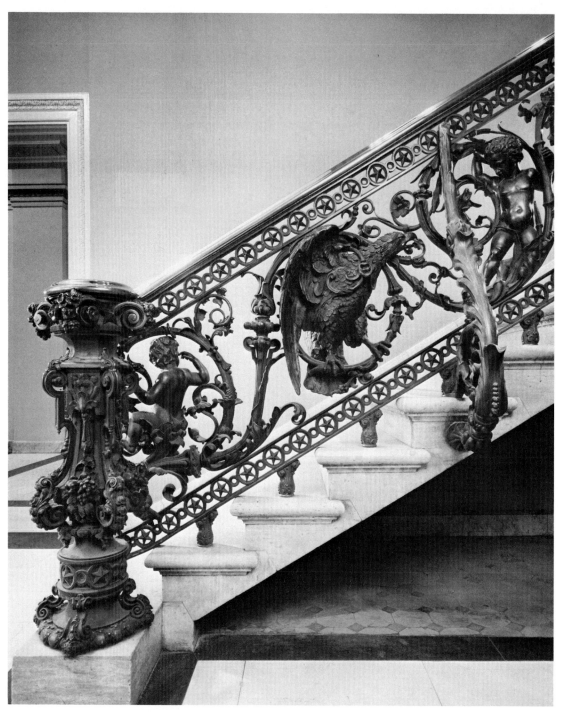

BALUSTERS AND RAILS
Designed by Constantino Brumidi, 1857, bronze
Two stairways in the Senate wing and two in the House wing are decorated with magnificent designs
in bronze. Modeled by Edmond Baudin and cast in Philadelphia by Archer, Warner, Miskey and
Co., 1857–59

Details of Bronze Stairways

NEG. NO. 37087

375

NEG. NO. 35114

CIRCULAR WINDOWS (4)
J. and G. H. Gibson Company of Philadelphia, 1859–60, 59″ diameter
First floor landing on each grand stairway

Three windows are emblazoned with the shield, eagle and flags of the United States and the motto, "E Pluribus Unum." The center of the window on the East Senate stairway was accidentally destroyed and was replaced with embossed glass.

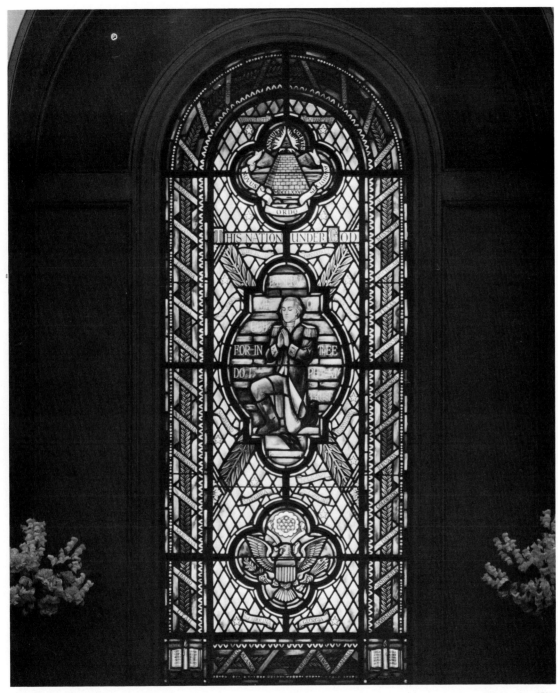

PRAYER WINDOW
Anonymous gift, 1955, 3′8½″ x 9′3⅜″
H–234

This window is the focal point of the small, private room which is used by Senators and Representatives for meditation. The seal of the United States, a biblical quotation, and the names of the fifty states surround the central figure of George Washington kneeling.

377

GEORGE WASHINGTON MEMORIAL WINDOW
Signed Maria Herndl; 1901, 39″ x 62¾″
Purchased 1910 by Joint Committee on the Library
Senators' private dining room, first floor

General Washington is pictured in conference with General Lafayette and Baron von Steuben in a Revolutionary War scene of 1780. This work of art was loaned to the Smithsonian Institution in 1932 where it was on display until 1962 when it was returned to the Capitol and installed in the dining room.

RECTANGULAR LAYLIGHTS (4)
J. and G. H. Gibson Company of Philadelphia, 1859–60
Grand stairways: House wing 2; Senate wing 2

Appendix I

Mantels
Models
Mottoes
Plaques
Centennial Safe

MANTELS

Reconstruction of the original North and South wings of the Capitol, burned by the British in 1814, was progressing rapidly when Charles Bulfinch became the third Architect of the Capitol in 1818. The work was being accomplished according to the designs of Bulfinch's predecessor, Benjamin Henry Latrobe, and had progressed to the point where Bulfinch had no viable alternative except to continue with that plan. Among the items that he inherited were fifty marble mantels that he installed between 1819 and 1829.

In spite of alterations, additions, fires and other vagaries of time that have occurred since the Latrobe and Bulfinch period, a number of the finest examples of mantel design of the Federal Period still exist as originally installed in the Capitol.

Notable among these are two finely carved marble mantels located in the Old Senate Chamber. These two resulted from an original order for four mantels, executed from drawings prepared by Giovanni Andrei at the direction of Latrobe. They were ordered from James Traquair in Philadelphia about 1812, but because of wartime shipping dangers, they were not sent to Washington, and thus were saved by their absence from the British incendiary fire of 1814. When the Capitol was rebuilt, these mantels, crated and waiting for three years, were installed and Traquair was paid $800 for them in 1817. The other two mantels that were part of the original order have never been located.

During the rebuilding of 1815–1819, six mantels were obtained from James Hodge of Albany, New York, and at least four others were purchased from the Milford Marble Co. of New Haven, Connecticut. The identities and locations of these mantels are not known.

By the time Thomas U. Walter became Architect of the Capitol in 1851 and designed the present dome and House and Senate wings, styles had changed. The slender reeding and vertical lines popular 50 years earlier had given way to the curving opulence of the Victorian Era, and these new styles were incorporated into the mantels of the new wings. At the same time, some occupants of the older central part of the building, who wished to be more in keeping with the times, had their earlier mantels removed and replaced with the new styles which had semicircular openings and, in some cases, grates for the burning of coal.

Several mantels of this later design may be found on the various floors of the West Central wing. That area was formerly occupied by the Library of Congress and rebuilt after a fire destroyed the Library in 1851. The Library moved to its new building in 1897, and in 1900 the space was reconstructed for offices.

In carrying out the work of extending the East Central Front, the mantels of the Old Senate Chamber were used as the inspiration for the designs of the new mantels in the Senate Conference Room and House Reception Room.

Selected photographs show examples of the many mantels now in the Capitol.

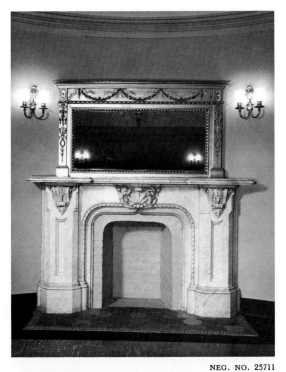

NEG. NO. 25711

Room HB–25
Thomas U. Walter, 1857

NEG. NO. 24202

Room H–110
Bulfinch period

NEG. NO. 24204

Room H–116
Bulfinch period

NEG. NO. 34363

Room H–150
Bulfinch period

383

Room H–151
Bulfinch period

Room H–162
Bulfinch period

Room H–157
Bulfinch period

Room H–163
Bulfinch period

Room H–164
Bulfinch period

Rayburn Room, H–207
East Front Extension, 1960

Room H–209
Thomas U. Walter, 1857

Room S–150
Bulfinch period

SENATE CONFERENCE ROOM, S–207
East Front Extension, 1960

SENATE MARBLE ROOM, S–215
Thomas U. Walter

OLD SENATE CHAMBER, S–228
Latrobe, 1812

OLD SENATE CHAMBER, S–228
Latrobe, 1812

MODELS OF UNITED STATES CAPITOL

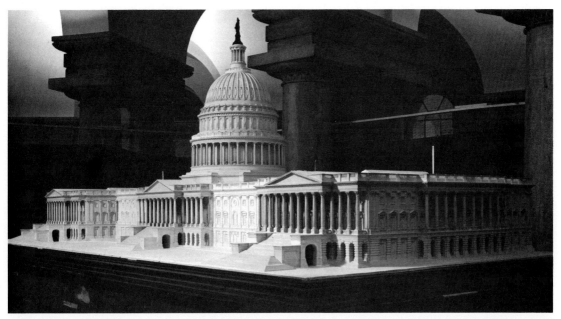

NEG. NO. 26357

EAST FRONT EXTENSION
Emile Garet, 1903–04
Length: 12' 7''; width: 5'9½''
Height: 4'9½'' (from platform to top of statue)
Base: 13'½'' x 6' x 4''
Scale: 100' = ⅛''

This study model in plaster was constructed by the Office of the Architect of the Capitol through the employment of Emile Garet, architectural sculptor, as part of a 1904 report for the extension and completion of the U.S. Capitol. Fifty-eight years later the East Front extension became a reality.

The model was constructed so that the extension could be removed to compare the Capitol as it then existed with the proposed changes of 1904. The delicate carvings and attention to detail caused it to be considered a work of art. It was sent to many expositions, among them the Panama Pacific International Exposition in San Francisco, California, 1915; the Sesquicentennial Exposition, Philadelphia, Pennsylvania, 1926; International Exposition, Seville, Spain, 1928–29, where it received a gold medal as the outstanding feature of the exhibit of the Commission of Fine Arts; and the Great Lakes Exposition, Cleveland, Ohio in 1937.

The much traveled model was placed on display in the Crypt of the Capitol from 1938 to 1976, when it was moved to the subway rotunda of the Cannon House Office Building.

WEST FRONT EXTENSION
Hadley Associates, Inc., 1966
Length: 47″; width: 22″
Height: 18″
Base: 4′ 8″ x 7′
Scale: $\frac{1}{16}$″ = 1′

This model is based on the plan for the Extension of the West Central Front recommended by Associate Architects and approved by the Commission for the Extension of the United States Capitol June 17, 1966. It is made of white metal or aluminum and acrylic plastic, with various materials used in the site surrounding the model. The walnut base and glass showcase were also made by the modeler.

The model is on display in the Crypt of the Capitol.

MOTTOES

These mottoes are incised in marble and are not illustrated.

In God We Trust. House Chamber, placed 1962 by House Res. 740, 87th Congress. Three stars behind the Speaker's rostrum were removed to place the inscription. The same motto is found in the Longworth House Office Building and the Dirksen Senate Office Building.

The following mottoes were added to the Senate Chamber when it was remodeled in 1950.

Annuit Coeptis. God has favored our undertakings. Over east doorway.

Novus Ordo Seclorum. A new order of the ages is born. Over west doorway.

In God We Trust. Over South entrance.

E Pluribus Unum. One out of many. Panel behind Vice President's chair.

PLAQUES AND MARKERS

A circular 3⅞ inch bronze marker on the floor of Statuary Hall (the Old Hall of the House) marks the place John Quincy Adams, then a Member of the House, had his desk. Here on February 21, 1848, he fell to the floor mortally ill and died two days later in a nearby room. The marker was placed in 1888. Not illustrated.

NEG. NO. 33886

Joseph G. Cannon, Speaker
Sculptor: Frank Eliscu, bronze, 28″ x 40″
Placed January 31, 1969
Cannon House Office Building rotunda

CONRAD AND McMUNN HOTEL
In storage, bronze

This plaque was removed in 1929 from the hotel which occupied the site of the Longworth House Office Building.

CIVIL WAR TROOPS
Placed December 17, 1965
by House Res. 530, 88th Congress,
bronze, 41¾″ x 55¾″
East Front entrance, first floor, House side

COMMEMORATING THE LAYING OF THE U.S. CAPITOL CORNERSTONE, 1793
Placed during George Washington Bicentennial, 1932, stone, 4′ x 2′ x 1′4″
Old Supreme Court entrance, first floor, East Front

NEG. NO. 24611

CENTENNIAL OF THE U.S. CAPITOL CORNERSTONE
Placed 1893, bronze, 53¾″ x 80″
Old Supreme Court entrance, first floor,
East Front

DECLARATION OF INDEPENDENCE
Gift of Michael Francis Doyle, 1932, bronze,
Rotunda

House of Representatives First Meeting Place in the Capitol
Placed 1952, bronze, 24"x 28"
Outside Senate Disbursing Office, S-233

LYNDON B. JOHNSON
Bronze, 10″ x 14″
Placed June 25, 1964
S–211

NEG. NO. 20486

IN GOD WE TRUST
Placed 1961, two identical bronzes
(1) Longworth House Office Building, main lobby, east wall
(2) Dirksen Office Building, southwest entrance, west wall

NEG. NO. 40510

THE JOHN W. McCORMACK ANNUAL AWARD OF EXCELLENCE
Designed by the Office of the Architect of the Capitol, bronze on mahogany, 31″ x 42″, placed December 17, 1970
Corridor opposite H–209, Speaker's Office

NEG. NO. 26728

JOHN F. KENNEDY
Bronze, 10″ x 14″
Placed June 30, 1964
S–210

THE FIRST SENATE CHAMBER
1800 — 1808

THIS TABLET MARKS THE LOCATION OF THE FIRST SENATE
CHAMBER IN THE CAPITOL. HERE, ON NOVEMBER 21, 1800,
THE SENATE MET FOR THE FIRST TIME IN WASHINGTON—
FOR THE SECOND SESSION OF THE SIXTH CONGRESS. HERE,
PRESIDENT JOHN ADAMS, ON NOVEMBER 22, 1800,
DELIVERED HIS LAST ANNUAL MESSAGE TO BOTH HOUSES.
HERE, THOMAS JEFFERSON, AFTER PRESIDING OVER THE
SENATE DURING THE SESSION, TOOK OATH OF OFFICE, ON
MARCH 4, 1801, FROM CHIEF JUSTICE JOHN MARSHALL,
AS PRESIDENT OF THE UNITED STATES AND DELIVERED
HIS FIRST INAUGURAL ADDRESS.

HERE, ON MARCH 4, 1805, PRESIDENT JEFFERSON
DELIVERED HIS SECOND INAUGURAL ADDRESS.

HERE THE SENATE CONTINUED TO MEET, PRESIDED OVER
BY VICE PRESIDENTS AARON BURR AND GEORGE CLINTON,
THROUGH THE FIRST SESSION OF THE TENTH CONGRESS,
ADJOURNED APRIL 25, 1808.

PRESENTED BY
THE NATIONAL CAPITAL SESQUICENTENNIAL COMMISSION
1951

NEG. NO. 11681

THE FIRST SENATE CHAMBER
Placed 1952, bronze 28¼″ x 24″
Original Center building, Senate wing, first floor

SPEAKER'S PLAQUE
Design: Paul W. Bartlett
Text: by Charles E. Fairman
Placed 1924, bronze, 12″ x 17″
Speaker's Lobby

SPEAKER SAM RAYBURN
Placed July 6, 1962, bronze, 15¾″ x 24¾″
House Reception Room, H–207

TELEGRAPH CENTENNIAL
Sculptor: Lee Lawrie, bronze, 34¾″ x 48¾″
Unveiled May 24, 1944
Center section, first floor

PRESIDENTS TREES

Gift: Maryland State Daughters of American Revolution, 1934, bronze on granite

Capitol Grounds, between Louisiana and Delaware Avenues, N.E.

Thirty-one trees were dedicated to 31 United States Presidents by the 31 Maryland Chapters of Daughters of the American Revolution as part of the Maryland Tercentenary.

ARTHUR H. VANDENBERG

Placed March 28, 1967, bronze, 10″ x 14″

S–138

GEORGE WASHINGTON'S HOUSES

Gift of District of Columbia, placed during George Washington Bicentennial, 1932, bronze on granite

Capitol Plaza fountain terrace

After serving as private homes to successive owners, the houses became hotels and were in greatly altered condition when they were razed in 1913.

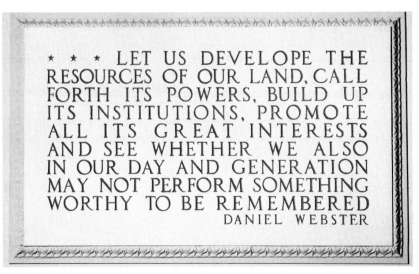

QUOTE FROM WEBSTER
Placed House Chamber 1949–50 at the time of its remodeling, marble
Above gallery door, south wall

Source: speech at the laying of the cornerstone of the Bunker Hill Monument at Charlestown, Boston, Mass. June 17, 1825.

HENRY WILSON, VICE PRESIDENT
Placed 1902, bronze, 10½" x 14½"
Vice President's Room, S–214

LINCOLN MARKER
Placed August 1, 1974, bronze, 7½″ x 7½″
Statuary Hall

SIGNERS OF THE DECLARATION OF INDEPENDENCE
Sculptor: Alan Robbins, bronze 62″ x 45½″
Accepted by Joint Committee on the Library
Unveiled March 20, 1976
East Front foyer, second floor

CENTENNIAL SAFE

As a feature of the Centennial Exposition in 1876 in Philadelphia, this safe was displayed as a patriotic gesture by Mrs. Charles F. Deihm, a publisher from New York. In it was placed a diversified collection of pictures and signatures of legislative, judicial, executive, business and civic leaders. Also included were memorabilia such as a silver Tiffany inkstand.

From Philadelphia the safe was brought to Washington in 1877 and placed in Statuary Hall. It was closed with ceremony on February 22, 1879 with the instructions it was to be opened "by the Chief Magistrate" in 1976. Shortly thereafter, it was placed under the east central portico for safekeeping.

As a feature of the Bicentennial celebration, the safe was opened July 1, 1976 by President Gerald Ford.

NEG. NO. 41169

CENTENNIAL SAFE
Manufactured by the Marvin Safe Company
Gift of Mrs. C. F. Deihm, 50" x 40" x 64"
Accepted by H. Con. Res. 84, 93d Congress

Appendix II

Works of Art Property of Committees
Works of Art Transferred
Works of Art Lost in Fires
Works of Art not Part of the Capitol Collection

WORKS OF ART PROPERTY OF COMMITTEES

NO PHOTOGRAPHS

With the exception of the House Appropriations Committee portraits, works of art acquired by the House and Senate Committees are not part of the Capitol collection. No records of them are maintained in the Office of the Architect of the Capitol, and as a result, this is only a partial listing.

House Agriculture Committee, 1301 Longworth House Office Building.

Harold D. Cooley by Mabel Pugh
John W. Flannagan by Dalton Shourds
Hampton P. Fulmer by Dalton Shourds
Clifford R. Hope by Mabel Pugh
Marvin Jones by Boris B. Gordon
W. R. Poage by Victor Lallier

House Armed Services Committee, 2118 Rayburn House Office Building.

Walter Gresham Andrews, plaster bust by Anna G. Dunbar
Walter G. Andrews by Robert O. Skemp
F. Edward Hébert by John C. Parker
Philip J. Philbin by Emily B. Waite
Melvin Price by Robert Templeton
L. Mendel Rivers by M. John Lenhardt
Dewey J. Short by Percy A. Leason
Carl Vinson by Lawrence Powers

House Banking and Currency Committee, 2128 Rayburn House Office Building.

Wright Patman by Victor Lallier
Brent Spence by Samuel C. Gholson
Henry B. Steagall by Howard Chandler Christy
Jesse Paine Wolcott, photograph by Shoaf

House District of Columbia Committee, 1310 Longworth House Office Building.

Charles C. Diggs, Jr. by Joseph D. Clipper
Everett M. Dirksen by Gisbert Palmie
John L. McMillan by Charles E. Hoover
Mary T. Norton by Elaine Hartley

House Government Operations Committee, 54 Rayburn House Office Building.

William L. Dawson by Robert B. Williams
Chester E. Holifield by Lloyd B. Embry

House Interior and Insular Affairs Committee, 1324 Longworth House Office Building.

Wayne N. Aspinall by Charles J. Fox
James A. Haley by Thornton Utz

House International Relations Committee, 2170 Rayburn House Office Building.

Sol Bloom by Howard Chandler Christy
Robert B. Chiperfield by Lloyd B. Embry
Charles A. Eaton by Alfred Jonniaux
Henry D. Flood by M. Hartman
Thomas S. Gordon
John Kee by Alfred Jonniaux
J. Charles Linthicum by Thomas C. Corner
Samuel Davis McReynolds by Henry Wolf
Thomas E. Morgan by Victor Lallier
James P. Richards by Charles C. Tucker

House Interstate and Foreign Commerce Committee, 2123 Rayburn House Office Building.

Oren Harris by Louis Freund
Harley O. Staggers by Charles J. Fox
Charles A. Wolverton by Charles Ricciardi

House Judiciary Committee, 2141 Rayburn House Office Building.

Emanuel Celler by Joseph Margulies
George S. Graham by Richard L. Partington
Hatton W. Sumners by Boris B. Gordon
Francis Thomas, photograph

House Merchant Marine and Fisheries Committee, 1334 Longworth House Office Building.

Schuyler O. Bland by Sandor C. Klein
Herbert C. Bonner by Mabel Pugh
Edward A. Garmatz by Charles J. Fox
Leonor K. Sullivan by Charles J. Fox

House Public Works Committee, 2167 Rayburn House Office Building.

Theodore E. Burton, plaster bust by Louise K. Sparrow
John A. Blatnik by William F. Draper
Charles A. Buckley by Osk Gruber
George A. Dondero by Dorothy H. Drew
George H. Fallon by Charles J. Fox
Robert E. Jones by Charles J. Fox
Joseph J. Mansfield by Boris B. Gordon
William M. Whittington by Karl Wolfe

House Rules Committee, H–313, Capitol.

Ray J. Madden by William J. Sabol
Howard V. Smith by Victor Lallier

House Science and Technology Committee, 2318 Rayburn House Office Building.

George P. Miller by Victor Lallier
Robert H. Goddard by Peter Stevens. Gift of National Space Club
Olin E. Teague by Terry Rodgers

House Small Business Committee, 2359 Rayburn House Office Building. The portraits are the work of artist Lloyd B. Embry.

Joseph L. Evins
William S. Hill
Wright Patman
Walter C. Ploeser

House Veterans' Affairs Committee, 334 Cannon House Office Building.

William J. Bryan Dorn by Robert B. Williams
Royal C. Johnson by Margaret Brisbine

John E. Rankin by Margaret Brisbine
Ray Roberts by Robert B. Williams
Edith N. Rogers by Howard C. Christy
Olin E. Teague by Ralph Chase

House Ways and Means Committee, 1102 Longworth House Office Building.

James W. Collier by Boris B. Gordon
Jere Cooper by Boris B. Gordon
Nelson Dingley, Jr. by unknown artist
Robert L. Doughton by Boris B. Gordon
Robert L. Doughton, photograph tinted in oil
Joseph W. Fordney, photograph tinted in oil
William R. Green by unknown artist
Willis C. Hawley by Boris B. Gordon
Claude Kitchen by Freeman Thorp
Harold Knutson by Thomas E. Stephens
William McKinley, Jr. by Freeman Thorp
Roger Q. Mills by unknown artist
Wilbur D. Mills by Boris B. Gordon
Sereno E. Payne by Cecilia Beaux
Daniel A. Reed by Jean Spencer
Oscar W. Underwood by Michel Jacobs

Albert Thomas Gymnasium, Rayburn House Office Building.

Albert Thomas by Victor Lallier

Senate Armed Services Committee, 212 Russell Senate Office Building.

Iwo Jima by Joseph Capolino

Senate Post Office and Civil Service Committee, 6200 Dirksen Senate Office Building.

Olin Johnston by Frank J. Crawford

House Republican Leaders

Charles A. Halleck
William J. Sabol, 1974
Signed l.r. Sabol
Gift of friends
Accepted by H. Res. 1477, 93rd Congress and the Joint Committee on the Library
H–227. No photograph

Leslie C. Arends
Signed 1.1. Everett Raymond Kinstler 1977; 38″ x 34″
Gift of friends
Accepted by H. Res. 1544, 94th Congress
H–227. No photograph

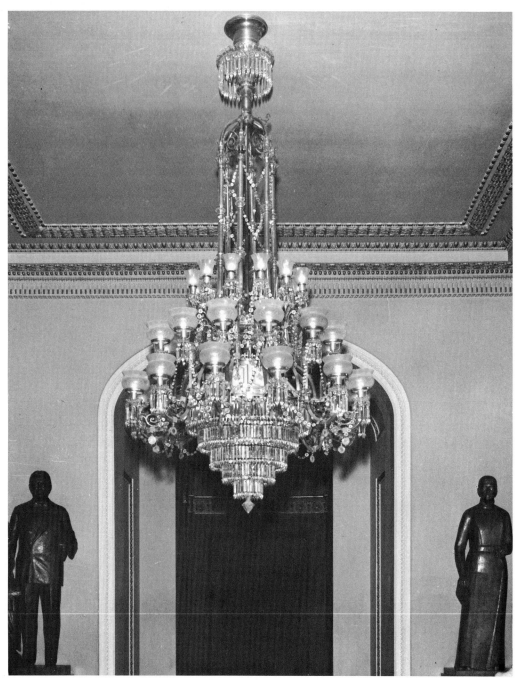

NEG. NO. 22469

CRYSTAL CHANDELIER

Transferred from the White House 1902–03. It hung in the Senate connecting corridor, second floor, until June 1962 when it was lent to the White House.

JOSEPH HENRY
Henry Ulke

Transferred to Smithsonian Institution, 1917 by
Senate Resolution 334, 64th Congress

BENJAMIN WEST
Self portrait
Purchased 1876

Transferred to Smithsonian Institution, 1917 by direction of the Joint Committee on the Library

MEDALS

About 1200 were damaged but not destroyed by the fire of 1851 in the Library of Congress, which was then in the Capitol. Joint Committee on the Library authorized the Librarian to present the medals to the Smithsonian Institution July 19, 1861. No photograph.

CHASM OF THE COLORADO
Thomas Moran, 12′ x 6′11″
Purchased 1874
   Transferred 1950 to the Department of Interior P.L. 603, 81st Congress

GRAND CANYON OF THE YELLOWSTONE
Thomas Moran, 11′11″ x 6′10″
Purchased 1872
   Transferred 1950 to the Department of Interior P. L. 603, 81st Congress

NEG. NO. 26185
Courtesy Virginia Military Institute

GENERAL WINFIELD SCOTT
Edward Troye
Purchased 1891

   Indefinite loan to Virginia Military Institute 1939, Public Resolution 21,
76th Congress

FARMING IN THE DAKOTAS
Carl Gutherz
Purchased March 3, 1887

   Transferred to the Department of Agriculture, 1888
by direction of the Joint Committee on the Library
No photograph

FIRST FIGHT OF THE IRONCLADS
William Formby Halsall
Purchased 1887

   Transferred to the United States Naval Academy
Annapolis, Maryland, 1946 by provision of P.L. 700
79th Congress. No photograph

FREEDOM, model
Thomas Crawford, plaster, 1858
   Transferred to Smithsonian Institution, 1890
Stored by Smithsonian, 1967

IL PENSEROSO
Joseph Mozier, marble, 1872
   Transferred 1888 by direction of the Joint Committee
on the Library to the National Museum, now the National Collection of Fine Arts, Smithsonian Institution.

408

TRIPOLI OR PEACE MONUMENT
Charles Micali, marble

Gift of Officers of the United States Navy to memorialize the losses of the Navy at Tripoli, 1803. Originally placed in the Navy Yard in Washington in 1808; moved to the west grounds of the Capitol 1831. Transferred to the United States Naval Academy at Annapolis, Maryland, 1860 (U.S. Stats. at Large, v. 12, p. 83).

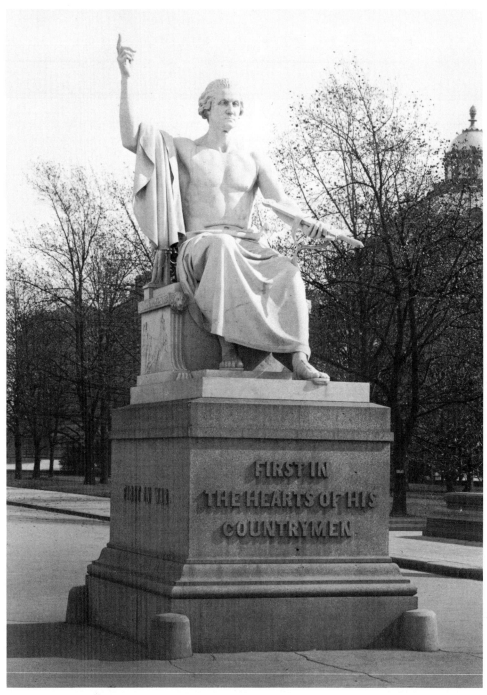

GEORGE WASHINGTON
Horatio Greenough, marble
Purchased 1833–36
Transferred to Smithsonian Institution 1908 by Pub. Res. No. 26

Installed in the Rotunda 1841 and moved to the east Capitol Grounds, 1844. The huge base became the cornerstone of the Capitol Power Plant.

410

GEORGE WASHINGTON.

The General Assembly of the Commonwealth
of Virginia have caused this Statue to be erected
as a monument of affection and gratitude to
GEORGE WASHINGTON:
who, uniting to the endowments of the *Hero*
the virtues of the *Patriot*, and exerting both
in establishing the Liberties of his Country
has rendered his name dear to his Fellow Citizens,
and given the world an immortal example
of true *Glory*. Done, in the year of
CHRIST,
One thousand seven hundred and eighty eight,
and in the year of the Commonwealth the twelfth.

GEORGE WASHINGTON
William J. Hubard after Antoine Houdon, plaster
Placed in 1850, accepted by Act of July 15, 1870

Transferred by P. L. 605, 81st Congress, July 11, 1950, to Smithsonian Institution.

411

WORKS OF ART LOST IN FIRES

Three major fires in the Capitol have caused the destruction of works of art. During the War of 1812 the British burned the Capitol on August 24, 1814. Furniture, books from the Library of Congress, paintings, portraits and sculpture were piled in the House and Senate Chambers and then put "to the torch."

The Library of Congress (in the Capitol from 1800 to 1897) was almost totally destroyed by an accidental fire December 24, 1851. Over three fifths of the books were burned and many paintings, portraits and busts were lost.

A fire on January 3, 1930 in a room used to make and store models caused some additional losses.

The accompanying chart is a composite listing of known items that are traditionally recorded as destroyed by fires, although the extant records are incomplete.

412

Subject	Item	Artist	Fire
John Adams [2]	Portrait	Gilbert Stuart	1851
John Quincy Adams	Bust	Luigi Persico	1851
John Quincy Adams	Portrait	J. Cranch	1851
Apollo	Bust or statue	Unknown artist	1851
Samuel Blodget, Jr.	Portrait	John Trumbull (?)	1930
Simon Bolivar	Portrait	Unknown artist	1851
Pietro Bonanni	Portrait	Self	1930
Christopher Columbus	Portraits (2)	Unknown artists	1851
Christopher Columbus	Bust	Giuseppe Ceracchi	1851
Hernando Cortez	Portrait	Unknown artist	1851
Baron De Kalb	Portrait	Unknown artist	1851
Judge C. D. Drake	Portrait	Charles Bittinger	1930
John Hanson	Portrait	Unknown artist	1851
F. Hapler	Bust, plaster	Unknown artist	1851
Ferdinand R. Hassler	Bust	Unknown artist	1851
Andrew Jackson	Bust, plaster	Unknown artist	1851
Thomas Jefferson	Bust, marble	Giuseppe Ceracchi	1851
Thomas Jefferson [2]	Portrait	Gilbert Stuart	1851
Thomas Jefferson	Statue	Unknown artist	1851
William Johnson	Portrait	Unknown artist	1851
Marquis de Lafayette	Bust, marble	David d'Angers	1851
Liberty and the Eagle	Statue	Giuseppe Franzoni	1814
Louis XVI [1]	Portrait	Madame Vigee Lebrun	1814
James Madison	Medallion	Unknown artist	1851
James Madison [2]	Portrait	Gilbert Stuart	1851
Marie Antoinette [1]	Portrait	Madame Vigee Lebrun	1814
John Marshall	Bust, plaster	Unknown artist	1851
James Monroe [2]	Portrait	Gilbert Stuart	1851
Governor Moultrie	Bust, plaster	Col. J. S. Cogdell	1851
Ogdall	Bust, plaster	Unknown artist	1851
Peyton Randolph	Portrait	Unknown artist	1851
Zachary Taylor	Bust, marble	Unknown artist	1851
Americus Vespucius	Bust	Giuseppe Ceracchi	1851
Baron Von Steuben	Portrait	Pyne	1851
George Washington	Bust	Giuseppe Ceracchi	1851
George Washington	Bust, bronze	David d'Angers	1851
George Washington [2]	Portrait	Gilbert Stuart	1851
L. Woodbury	Bust, plaster	Unknown artist	1851

[1] These portraits disappeared in 1814, but it is not known whether they were burned or sent out prior to the fire to be repaired and were never returned.

[2] Owned by Mr. Phelps of Boston.

WORKS OF ART NOT PART OF THE CAPITOL COLLECTION

The Joint Committee on the Library has not accepted these works of art. Some are gifts, some have been left by owners who cannot be located. Any existing records are maintained by the Architect of the Capitol. For many, the records are incomplete or the works cannot be found.

Subject	Item	Artist	Location
Jean Louis R. Agassiz, Swiss-American naturalist	Portrait	Henry Ulke	Location unknown, Purchased 1877
Harold R. Beckley, Superintendent of Senate Press Gallery	Photograph tinted in oil	Gladys A. Kazigian	Press Room, Dirksen Office Building. Gift from Correspondents' Committee.
Theodore E. Burton, Representative and Senator from Ohio	Bust, plaster	Louise Kidder Sparrow	In storage Gift of the artist,
Archibald Willingham Butt, Major, United States Army	Portrait, 40″ x 60″	Harold L. Macdonald about 1923	In storage No records
Joseph G. Cannon, Speaker of the House of Representatives	Portrait	Michel Jacobs	244 Cannon House Office Building
Joseph G. Cannon	Portrait	George Burroughs Torrey	In storage
Carpenter's Hall	Painting, 38⅜″ x 50⅜″	Charles McVickers, 1967	HB–29. Presented to House of Representatives September 25, 1974 by U.S. Capitol Historical Society.
Subject unknown. Sometimes referred to as Columbus	Bust, plaster 29½″	Unknown artist	HB–28 No records
Downwind Victory	Painting, 25⅜″ x 30⅜″	Bruce E. Roberts, 1973	H–125. Gift of artist to House of Representatives May 10, 1973
Charles E. Fairman, First Art Curator of the Capitol	Portrait 24½″ x 29½″	Nicholas R. Brewer	HB–28. Gift of Mr. Fairman
Flowers of Joy	Painting 35½″ x 47½″	Beatrice Van Wye	H–311. Presented to House of Representatives May 15, 1968 in honor of Congressional wives. Accepted by Speaker John W. McCormack
Thomas Hendricks, Representative and Senator from Indiana and Vice President	Portrait	Unknown artist	Location unknown
Abraham Lincoln	Bust, bronze	Unknown artist	Location unknown Gift of Col. A. DeGroot, 1871
Abraham Lincoln	Portrait	Griswold Tyng	S–113. Gift of Senator Kenneth S. Wherry's family, 1952

Subject	Item	Artist	Location
John T. Morgan Senator from Alabama	Portrait	Carl Gutherz, 1893	S–339. Offered by Senator Morgan's daughter, 1910
Justin Morrill Representative and Senator from Vermont	Portrait	Carl Gutherz	Location unknown
Franklin Delano Roosevelt	Portrait	Unknown artist	In storage. Presented by National Italian American Civic League, 1937
Seascape	Painting, 30″ x 50″	John D. Wisinski	H–130. Gift of Representative John C. Kluczynski to House of Representatives January 26, 1972. Accepted by Speaker Carl Albert
Morris Sheppard Representative and Senator from Texas	Portrait	B. Godwin, 1939	In Storage. No records
Robert A. Taft Senator from Ohio	Portrait	Rudolph Bernatschke, 1953	S–229. Gift of the artist, 1959
Nicholas Van Dyke, Jr. Senator from Delaware	Portrait	Jefferson D. Chalfant	S–209. Presented to the Senate in 1914 by great granddaughters of Senator Van Dyke
Uncle Sam '76	Statuette, plaster, 21½″	Attributed to Horatio Stone	HB–28. No records
United States Capitol, East Front	Painting, watercolor, 35½″ x 81½″	Hughson Hawley, 1905	Corridor, across from SB–15. Purchased 1905
United States Capitol Extension, East Front	Painting	Robert Kirwan, 1960	SB–16. Gift of Chesapeake and Potomac Telephone Company, 1961
United States Capitol, West Front	Painting, after an 1840 engraving by Bartlett, 23″ x 28″	Unknown artist, about 1850	SB–15. Gift of John C. Stevens, 1946
United States Senate, A.D. 1850	Engraving		S–224. Gift of United States Capitol Historical Society, 1964
Victory: U.S.S. Constitution After the Battle With the Guerriere	Painting	Gilbert T. Margeson, about 1905	H–104. No records
Thomas J. Walsh Senator from Montana	Bust, plaster	Louise Kidder Sparrow	Location unknown. Gift of artist
Thomas U. Walter 4th Architect of the Capitol.	Portrait	Eloise L. Everson,	In storage. Gift of artist
Daniel Webster Addressing the United States Senate on the Compromise Measures, March 7, 1850	Engraving	R. Van Dien, 1856	HB–28. No records
Daniel Webster	Portrait, 23″ x 31″	Francis H. Cumberland, 1961	S–146. Gift of artist

Appendix III

Floor Plans

The works of art in this book are located by room numbers and area names. By using the room designations given with each description in the text, their locations in the Capitol may be determined on the following floor plans.

Rooms to the left of the center are in the House wing and their numbers are preceded by an "H". Rooms to the right of the center are in the Senate wing and their numbers are preceded by an "S".

BASEMENT AND TERRACE FLOOR PLAN

MODELS OF HOUSE TYMPANUM

SENATE WING

HOUSE WING

MEZZANINE

MEZZANINE

COURT

COURT

SUB-BASEMENT

BOOK CONVEYOR TUNNEL

SCALE: 0 16 32 48 64 FEET

NORTH

O.I.P. 1971.

SUBWAY TERMINAL

SUBWAY TERMINAL

TO R.O.B.

TO D.O.B.

TO R.H.O.B.

TO C.H.O.B. & L.H.O.B.

FIRST FLOOR PLAN

SCALE: 0 16 32 48 64 FEET

O.I.P. 1971.

SECOND FLOOR PLAN

scale: 0 16 32 48 64 feet

NORTH

O.P. 1971

420

THIRD FLOOR PLAN

scale: 0   16   32   48   64   feet

O.I.P. 1971.   NORTH

WEST PORTICO

S-223 S-222 S-221 S-220 S-219

S-224 S-216

S-217

J. HANCOCK
(statue)

W. McKINLEY

C. FAIRBANKS S-225 PRESIDENT'S
ROOM
S-218

G. HOBART J. GARFIELD

LOGGIA L. MORTON

A. BARKLEY

SENATE
CONNECTING
CORRIDOR

SENATE
CHAMBER

SENATE LOBBY

NORTH PORTICO

S-215

A. STEVENSON

S-207

T. ROOSEVELT

V.P. FORMAL
OFFICE
S-214
L. FOSTER (Senator)
H. WILSON

J. SHERMAN S-226

C. HULL
(Senator)

LOGGIA B. FRANKLIN
(statue) H. TRUMAN C. CURTIS C. DAWES

SENATE RECEPTION ROOM

S-213 H. WALLACE
J. GARNER

S-208

ELEVATOR LOBBY

S-211 S-212

S-209 S-210

C. COOLIDGE T. MARSHALL

EAST PORTICO

STEPS DOWN

0   16   32   48 FT.
N

SENATE WING, SECOND FLOOR, SHOWING LOCATIONS OF BUSTS AND STATUES

422

WEST PORTICO

S-323   S-322   S-321   S-319   S-318

S-324

S-320   S-317

W. KING   J. CALHOUN

G. DALLAS   R. JOHNSON

H. HAMLIN   E. GERRY

S-316

S. COLFAX   A. BURR

SENATE EAST WEST CORRIDOR

LOGGIA

C. ARTHUR   J. ADAMS

UPPER PART OF SENATE CHAMBER

S-315

S-325

NORTH PORTICO

T. HENDRICKS   T. JEFFERSON

SENATE DOCUMENT ROOM

S-308

W. WHEELER   G. CLINTON

S-314

D. TOMPKINS

A. JOHNSON

M. FILLMORE

J. BRECKINRIDGE   J. TYLER

LOGGIA

A. LINCOLN   C. SUMNER   M. VAN BUREN

S-309

S-313

J. JONES   T. CRAWFORD

S-312

S-310   S-311

Z. TAYLOR   AYSH-KE-BAH-KE-KO-ZHAY

J. BRYCE   BEESHEKEE

O.I.P

EAST PORTICO

0   16   32   48   64 FT.

N

SENATE WING, THIRD FLOOR, SHOWING LOCATIONS OF BUSTS

423

CRYPT, FIRST FLOOR, SHOWING LOCATION OF STATUARY AND BUSTS

NATIONAL STATUARY HALL, HOUSE WING, SECOND FLOOR, SHOWING LOCATIONS OF STATUES IN THE HALL, THE ADJACENT CONNECTING CORRIDOR AND THE SMALL HOUSE ROTUNDA

THE ROTUNDA, SECOND FLOOR, SHOWING LOCATIONS OF PAINTINGS, STATUES AND BUSTS

OLD SENATE WING, SECOND FLOOR, SHOWING THE STATUES IN THE STATUARY HALL COLLECTION

HALL OF COLUMNS, HOUSE WING, FIRST FLOOR, SHOWING LOCATIONS OF STATUES IN THE STATUARY HALL COLLECTION

Old Senate Wing, first floor, showing busts and other art work

429

INDEX

Illustrations are indicated in bold face type

434

435

442

444

445

448

449

451

☆ U. S. GOVERNMENT PRINTING OFFICE : 1978 O - 78-299